FINGERTIP + MATH

How to use an electronic calculator to put speed, accuracy and confidence into everyday mathematics.

Edward M. Roberts

in collaboration with the
Texas Instruments Learning Center

Radio Shack
A Tandy Corp. Company

FINGERTIP MATH has been prepared primarily for operation of conventional four-function (add, subtract, multiply, and divide) calculators employing algebraic logic (enter the problem as you say it), and having an 8-digit display with full floating decimal. Some modification to the sequence of entry may be required on business and accounting-type machines in order to solve the example problems used in this book.

TABLE OF CONTENTS

Page

Introduction . . . . *viii*
How to Use a Calculator *1*
Chapter 1 – Getting Acquainted 3
  Addition 5
  The Clear Keys 5
  Multiplication and Division 6
  The Subtraction Key 12
  Function Key Errors 16
  The Decimal Point 18
  The Maximum Capacity 19
  Multiplication and Division with Zero 22
  Negative Zero 23
  Automatic Squaring 24
Chapter 2 – The Constant Key 29
  Division 35
  Mixed Chain and Constant Calculation 38
Chapter 3 – Reciprocals, Powers, and Roots . . . 41
  Reciprocals 41
  Powers of Numbers 44
  Negative Powers 47
  Fractional Exponents 48
  Finding Square Roots 48
  Finding Cube and Higher Roots 60

TABLE OF CONTENTS (Continued)

Page

Basic Arithmetic and the Electronic Calculator . . .   65
  Chapter 4 – The Number System   67
    Addition, Subtraction, and Negative Numbers. .   70
    Pencil and Paper Arithmetic   77
  Chapter 5 – Numbers Less Than One   93
    Decimal Fractions   93
    Significant Places and Rounding Off   103
    Common Fractions   110
    Summary   134
  Chapter 6 – Percentage   135
  Chapter 7 – Exponents, Powers, and Roots . . .   141
    Learning More   151
Applications   153
  Chapter 8 – Areas of Plane Figures   155
    The Rectangle   155
    The Right Triangle   156
    The Parallelogram   161
    The Acute Triangle   163
    The Obtuse Triangle   165
    Other Four-Sided Figures   167
    The Circle   170
    The Ellipse   174
    The Regular Polygon   176
    Polygon Values   178
    Odd and Unusual Shapes   179

TABLE OF CONTENTS (Concluded)

Page

Chapter 9 — Volumes, Capacities, and Weights . . . 185
   Rectangular Boxes (Parallelepiped) 185
   The Cylinder 187
   The Prism 188
   The Pyramid and Cone 189
   The Sphere 189
   Weights of Some Common Substances 193
   Some Practice Problems 194
   Specific Gravity 199
   The Metric System 199
Chapter 10 — Interest 203
   Installment Loans 204
   Home Mortgage 209
   Earned Interest 211
Appendix I — How to Use Some Common
Mathematical Tables 217
Appendix II — Operating the Calculator
by Touch 241
Appendix III — Summary of Other Features 259

INTRODUCTION

The brain of one average man is a more powerful and complex reasoning mechanism than all of the world's computers put together. Even at such a relatively simple task as chess playing, no one has succeeded in designing a computer capable of beating a human chess master consistently. But there is a major difference between a computer, which is designed to deal with many small, accurate facts, and the human brain, which evolved over millions of years under conditions requiring judgments, estimates, and approximations. A driver smoothly braking for a red light solves a highly complex problem over and over with one small corner of his brain. He is hardly aware of the effort. But ask that same driver to multiply 23 by 37, a problem that one tiny integrated circuit can solve in a few thousandths of a second, and without a pencil and paper he is likely to be completely baffled.

Numbers are an invention of civilized man, and working with them has made possible many of the technological advances we enjoy. But most human minds are still apparently ill-adapted to deal efficiently with numbers. Fortunately, in this electronic age, we can free the mind for more important things. Asking the human brain to do arithmetic is, in certain respects, like chartering a Greyhound bus to carry a baby across the street. A baby carriage can do a far better job in much less time.

The ideal scheme is to use the mind for what it can do better than any machine, and use electronics for one of the things it can do better than most minds. A combination of the great *conceptual* powers of the human brain and the *detail-handling* capacity of electronics makes a partnership of unlimited potential. It was the transistorized computer that finally put Man on the moon. The theory had been laid out centuries ago by Isaac Newton. The rest was scaled-up Chinese fireworks and some very elaborate technological craftsmanship.

It's fair to say that man took his first step toward the moon thousands of years ago, when he first began to count things. For a million years or so before that, men existed as roaming hunters – and hunters have little use for numbers. There are primitive tribes of hunters surviving today who have words for the numbers "one," "two," and "three," but no larger number. Any more than three, they call "many."

But as men settled down to farming and herding, they became dimly aware of a need for numbers, and a way to deal with them. The very word "calculate" comes from the Latin word "calculus," meaning a pebble used in reckoning. Shepherds, for example, customarily let one pebble represent each sheep in the flock; this was a simple but effective way to keep track of births, sales, and other transactions. Such pebbles on strings or rods probably provided the first abacus, a calculating device still being used effectively in some modern cultures.

The machine age brought calculating devices that used gears, levers, and cams instead of pebbles. This was a major breakthrough, and gave rise to a welter of mechanical adding machines, comptometers, and calculators. At first, they were cranked by hand; later, electric motors did the cranking. Many of these electromechanical calculators are still in use.

Now comes the Age of Electronics, heralding a whole new era in the history of man's manipulation of numbers. Soon after the transistor was invented in 1948, it was put to work handling numbers. When Texas Instruments made the silicon transistor a commercial reality in 1954, it became possible for the first time to operate electronic number-handling devices — computers — in such hostile environments as aircraft and spacecraft. A few office calculators were built using transistors, but so many separate devices had to be wired together that transistorized calculators were as large as their mechanical brothers, and expensive.

The world still waited for a significant breakthrough. It came in 1958, when Jack Kilby of Texas Instruments invented the integrated circuit — an achievement that earned him the National Medal of Science in 1969. Today's integrated circuit can perform the same number-handling functions as thousands of transistors — with the connections already made — on a tiny chip of silicon. This was the development that spawned the Calculator Revolution. This is the development that makes possible a calculator with all the power of a bulky, expensive, slow mechanical calculator — yet one that fits in a pocket, that anybody can afford, and that solves problems with nearly the speed of light.

Curiously enough, modern electronic calculators as well as computers have at their working heart one vital ingredient, the element silicon. And so do pebbles.

An electronic pocket calculator is the simplest member of the family of computers. Yet in knowledgeable hands, it's surprisingly powerful. Here's an example: When Napier invented logarithms in 1614, he simplified and expedited computation. This caused a revolution in mathematics comparable to the computer revolution of today. The following bit of arithmetic, solved by *primitive* means, requires the writing of 223 numerals and 8 to 10 minutes of tedious and error-prone work:

$$\frac{9.81 \times 3.04 \times .06 \times 17^4}{1.418} = 105{,}393.36$$

The use of *logarithms* eliminates three-fourths of the work and cuts the time to about $2\frac{1}{2}$ minutes. But the pocket *calculator* can do the same job in only 20 seconds, with no "scratch" notes!

Recognize the potential of this. Armed with a calculator, you can focus on solving problems and determining relationships. You're free of the hated drudgery of working long-division problems and recalling endless lists of multiplication facts. Instead, your tough and inexpensive little calculator will handle these uninspiring tasks. Your mind will be freed to enjoy the beauty and clarity of mathematics.

The ease and speed of calculator arithmetic makes it refreshingly different from "pencil-and-paper" arithmetic. The goal of any computation is to obtain a useable answer in minimum time. With a calculator, computation is instantaneous and accurate, whereas pencil-and-paper computation costs dearly in terms of time and effort. Since computation is so fast and effortless using a calculator, it can be good technique to use such "brute force" approaches as successive approximation, educated guesswork, and trial and error.

This in no way advocates carelessness and sloppy thinking. Quite the contrary, the calculator can aid in encouraging exploration and experimentation. It can stimulate and satisfy intellectual curiosity. We learn not only by being told, but by trying and failing, then trying again. Throughout this book, the emphasis is on "learning by doing." The reader is urged in the strongest possible way to make using a calculator a part of reading the book. There is a definite advantage in following every explanation on a calculator, and checking results against those given.

Many who buy calculators today are those who must learn in adulthood the skills that children one day will take for granted. Some believe they are "no good at math" and have bought calculators to compensate for that supposed deficiency. This book will demonstrate that calculator arithmetic is a simple, enjoyable skill which can be mastered by anyone. Our goal is to be useful to a wide range of users.

The first section of the book explains the use of the calculator in general terms — how to integrate it into one's thinking. It tells how to explore the powers of the calculator, since it has many capabilities that are not apparent at first glance.

The second section is a compact course in basic arithmetic utilizing the calculator. This section will be particularly valuable to elementary and high school students as well as to adults who feel they are deficient in their basic arithmetic skills. It is worth a glance even to those who feel comfortable with basic arithmetic, for it contains some calculator techniques which may not be self-apparent.

The third section contains practical information which will help in applying the calculator to the solving of some real-life mathematical problems.

A collection of useful tables is given in Appendix I.

A brief course on operating the calculator by touch, a skill of great usefulness, will be found in Appendix II.

Appendix III discusses some features which various small calculators may have in addition to the four basic functions.

The incredible powers of electronics have once again been harnessed to the everyday needs of the average man. No one can yet see clearly what changes this will bring. But it is clear that a great human adventure is just beginning, and that you are among the first to join it. Welcome aboard!

HOW TO USE A CALCULATOR

CHAPTER 1
GETTING ACQUAINTED

Let's get started by considering what a calculating device does for us, whether that device is our fingers, a slide rule, or an electronic calculator. No matter which one is selected, three basic steps must be followed:

1. Some numbers must be put down, or entered, perhaps by making marks on paper, perhaps by shifting beads on an abacus, or by throwing some electrical switches.
2. These numbers are then combined, using some rule of arithmetic.
3. The result is recorded for use.

For example:

Step 1, the numbers: 17 and 22	17
Step 2, the rule: addition	+22
Step 3, the result: 39	39

The electronic calculator must go through these same three steps. Let's identify the parts of the calculator which perform these steps:

The *keyboard* is used to "write" or enter numbers into the calculator.

The *display* records the numbers as they are entered. The display is also used to record the result after a calculation is complete. This double action makes it possible for the answer to one problem to be used as the first number of the next problem.

The *storage* holds one of the two numbers, while the other is in the display.

The *processor* is the real heart of the calculator. It combines the numbers in the display with those in storage according to the rule you select when you push a function key such as +, −, X, or ÷.

At this point we are going to start studying the calculator itself, but first we want to urge you to have a calculator at hand. The best possible way to learn is to actually *do* what you are learning. Throughout this book there are many opportunities for the reader who has a calculator to practice, using the examples shown. You should follow every explanation on a calculator, perform each calculation, and check your results against those shown. If you have access to a calculator, use it as your study companion.

Since calculators differ in the manner in which numbers and operations are entered, we shall limit our discussion to those calculators which use *algebraic* logic. (For a more complete description, see Appendix III).

In our discussion, we shall use some special symbols so that we can avoid telling you over and over how to use your calculator. Whenever symbols are printed in **bold** type, it means those entries are to be *made* into your calculator: **18** + **23** =

Whenever numbers are printed in *lighter* type, it means your calculator should *display* that result. If it does, you will know you have performed the operation correctly: **18** +
23 = 41

In contrast to algebraic logic, some pocket calculators follow office machine practice, and have keys marked $\boxed{+=}$ and $\boxed{-=}$ rather than having separate $\boxed{+}$, $\boxed{-}$ and $\boxed{=}$ keys. If your calculator is set up in this fashion, a brief review of your owners manual should resolve many difficulties.

So, if you have a calculator, switch it on and let's go exploring. The CHAIN-CONSTANT switch, if you have one, should be checked to make sure it is in the *Chain* position.

ADDITION

Using the calculator to add is so simple and straightforward that no instruction is necessary. The appropriate keys are merely pressed in the order in which we think of the problem:

"Five"   "plus"   "six"   "equals"   eleven

$\boxed{5}$ $\boxed{+}$ $\boxed{6}$ $\boxed{=}$ 11

Some remarkable things go on inside the calculator, but we'll examine these in the discussion of multiplication and division — the areas where the electronic calculator is so dramatically superior to any other calculating device.

THE CLEAR KEYS

Clear keys are necessary at times, and most calculators are provided with two of them. The key which is usually marked $\boxed{c}$ is straightforward; it simply wipes out everything in the calculator and leaves you with a clean slate. After clearing the display will usually exhibit a single zero, followed by a decimal point. This is mainly to remind you that the calculator is turned on. Some calculators require that the $\boxed{c}$ key be operated when the calculator is first switched on.

It is worth noting briefly that most calculators do not have to be cleared between many types of calculations. Perform both of the following calculations, but do not use the $\boxed{c}$ key between them:

$$2 \boxed{+} 2 \boxed{=} 4$$
$$3 \boxed{+} 3 \boxed{=} 6$$

Note how the calculator cleared itself, if it did.

Almost all calculators are provided with a second key, marked $\boxed{CE}$ (for "clear entry") or $\boxed{CD}$ (for "clear display").

This key allows us to correct an error in an *entry* without erasing earlier information put into the calculator. Let's say that you wished to add 56 and 33, but you entered 34 by mistake:

$$56 \boxed{+} 34 \boxed{CE} 33 \boxed{=} 89$$

Note that the 34 was erased, but the 56 and the instruction were left undisturbed.

MULTIPLICATION AND DIVISION

We are going to take the model problem of 56 times 33, and examine what happens inside the calculator. Enter the number 56. This action puts the 56 into the display, and the calculator looks like this:

The next step is to tell the calculator which rule of arithmetic we want it to follow. In this case it is the rule for multiplication, so we press the ⌈x⌋ key, and the calculator looks like this:

The ⌈x⌋ key made two things happen. The 56 is now in storage as well as in the display, and the ⌈x⌋ instruction has been remembered. Now press the key to enter 33:

This action removed the 56 from display, replacing it with the 33. The problem of 56 × 33 is now completely stated. In order to obtain the answer, press the ⌈=⌋ key:

The result of 1848 is now in display, but it is also in storage. This seems to be a rather strange arrangement. Why should the result of a problem be stored when it is also in display? The answer is that this arrangement makes possible one of the most valuable features of the calculator, the ability to do *chain* calculations. To see how this works, leave the previous result of 1848 in the calculator. Now press the ÷ key:

Now enter a **4** and notice that it replaces the 1848 in display, but that the 1848 remains in storage.

A new problem of 1848 ÷ 4 is now in position, ready to be calculated. Press the ⌷=⌷ key:

The answer, 462, is again sent to both storage and display, and the calculator is ready for a new link in a chain calculation. But what if we don't want to continue the chain? What if we want to begin an entirely new problem? Let's try it and see. Do *not* operate the ⌷c⌷ key. Just enter 19:

The 19 has replaced the 462 in display, just as we expected, but there is no operating instruction, so we press the ⌧ key. But, you will recall, pressing a function key makes the display number go into storage, with the result that the old, unwanted 462 simply disappears from the calculator:

Now, if we enter a 5, it replaces the 19 in display, and the entirely new problem of 19 × 5 is set up:

Finally, we press the = key, and again the result goes to both storage and display.

Thus we have a pair of rules:

*When a result is followed by an **instruction**, the chain continues.*

*When a result is followed by a **number** entry, an entirely new calculation begins.*

With these two rules in mind, you may want to go back and reread the material given just above the rules. This will help you in your understanding.

With this convenient feature of automatic clearing available, there is no point in your operating the $\boxed{c}$ key when it is not necessary. Do the following practice problems, keeping in mind the processes of chain calculation and automatic clearing. It is not necessary to use the $\boxed{c}$ key at any point in this series of problems:

$$1234 \boxed{\times} 9 \boxed{+} 5 \boxed{=} 11111$$
$$12345 \boxed{\times} 9 \boxed{+} 6 \boxed{=} 111111$$
$$16 \boxed{+} 61 \boxed{=} 77$$
$$14 \boxed{+} 41 \boxed{=} 55$$

THE SUBTRACTION KEY

The subtraction key deserves some special attention. Usually we think of subtraction as taking a smaller number away from a larger one, for instance:

$$67 \boxed{-} 12 \boxed{=} 55$$

However, it is much more useful to think of subtraction as being the adding of a negative number. (If you are not familiar with the idea of negative numbers, you should interrupt this description and read the review of subtraction in Chapter 4.) When the $\boxed{-}$ key in the calculator is operated, it does two things:

1) It gives the next number entered a negative value. The negative sign becomes visible on the display as soon as the entry is made.
2) It actuates the ADD instruction.

The operation $67 - 12 = 55$ is often thought of as "sixty-seven minus twelve equals fifty-five," but the calculator handles it as if it were "sixty-seven plus negative-twelve." The rules of addition say that numbers may be added in any order, yet produce the same result. That is, $2 + 4 = 6$, and also $4 + 2 = 6$. If the calculator is really adding negative numbers instead of subtracting, it should make no difference what order the numbers are entered. Let's try it:

67 ⬚ 12 ⬚ 55

ⓒ ⬚ 12 ⬚ 67 ⬚ 55

The result is the same in both cases. Note, however, the special need to operate the $\boxed{c}$ key before beginning the second problem. If this were not done, the calculator would interpret the operation of the $\boxed{-}$ key as being an instruction to chain the two problems together, yielding:

$$67 \boxed{-} 12 \boxed{=} 55 \boxed{-} 12 \boxed{+} 67 \boxed{=} 110$$

Therefore, if a new problem starts with a negative entry, it is necessary to operate the $\boxed{c}$ key.

When adding positive and negative numbers together, the result will sometimes be negative. When this happens, the calculator correctly displays the result:

$$42 \boxed{-} 83 \boxed{=} -41$$

This is a most useful feature where the work involves intermixed positive and negative numbers, as in balancing a checkbook. If you are accustomed to a mechanical adder which will say that 9 − 10 = 99,999,999, you should be alert for the appearance of the negative sign in the display.

The negative key can also be used to give a number a negative value in multiplication or division. Perform the following operations and note that the result is shown correctly:

$$22 \boxed{x} 9 \boxed{=} 198$$
$$\boxed{c} \boxed{-} 22 \boxed{x} \boxed{-} 9 \boxed{=} 198$$
$$\boxed{c} \boxed{-} 22 \boxed{x} 9 \boxed{=} -198$$
$$22 \boxed{x} \boxed{-} 9 \boxed{=} -198$$

Verify on your calculator that the correct results are shown in the *division* of negative numbers, using the same four combinations. The rules for the signs are the same in division as they are in multiplication, that is, two negatives make a positive, but when there is only one negative, the result is negative.

The negative key can also be used to change the sign of a number in the display. To either insert or remove the negative sign, perform:

$$\boxed{x}\ \boxed{-}\ 1$$

Here is an example:

$$31\ \boxed{+}\ 17\ \boxed{=}\ 48\ \boxed{x}\ \boxed{-}\ 1\ \boxed{=}\ -48\ \boxed{x}\ \boxed{-}\ 1\ \boxed{=}\ 48$$

Notice the bracket which appears over the set of three entries required to change the sign. This bracket is to make it clear to you the purpose of these entries. You should remember that in our calculator arithmetic the symbol $\boxed{x}\ \boxed{-}\ 1$ means "change the sign in display."

In summary, then, it seems most useful to think of the negative key as being a kind of combination key which does two things:

1) It puts some extra information into a number giving it a negative value

2) It operates the ADD instruction (provided the ADD instruction is not overridden by the $\boxed{x}$ or $\boxed{\div}$ key as described next).

This is a good time for a little recreation. Let's look at a numerical situation which has some rather interesting features.

Take any number, add to it that same number stated backwards, then repeat the process with the result as many times as necessary. You will always end up with a number that reads the same way forwards or backwards. For example:

789 + 987 = 1776
+ 6771 = 8547
+ 7458 = 16005
+ 50061 = 66066

FUNCTION KEY ERRORS

Sometimes an arithmetic function key is pressed in error. It is useful to know which keys will cancel other keys. In this way a correction can be made without copying the number in display and starting all over again. The ce key will not cancel an operating instruction; it will only cancel the last *number* entry made.

Each of the keys for the two operations, + and −, will cancel the other, depending on which was entered last:

8 − + 6 = 14
8 + − 6 = 2

The keys for x and ÷ will cancel each other, with the function entered last being used:

8 ÷ x 2 = 16
8 x ÷ 2 = 4

The keys for the complex operations will also cancel the $+$ key:

$$8 \boxed{+} \boxed{\times} 6 \boxed{=} 48$$
$$8 \boxed{+} \boxed{\div} 2 \boxed{=} 4$$

However the keys for the complex operations will *not* cancel the $\boxed{-}$ key, and the $\boxed{-}$ key will not cancel either the $\boxed{\times}$ or $\boxed{\div}$ key. If this were not true, there would be no way to give a number a negative value in multiplication or division:

$$8 \boxed{\times} \boxed{-} 6 \boxed{=} -48$$
$$8 \boxed{-} \boxed{\times} 6 \boxed{=} -48$$

However, if the $\boxed{-}$ key is pressed in error when the $\boxed{\times}$ or $\boxed{\div}$ key is intended, merely press the $\boxed{+}$ key to cancel the $\boxed{-}$ key, then proceed with the multiplication or division:

$$8 \boxed{-} \text{ (oops, I meant } \boxed{\times} \text{)} \boxed{+} \boxed{\times} 2 \boxed{=} 16$$

This covers all the possibilities except how to cancel the $\boxed{\times}$ or $\boxed{\div}$ key when addition or subtraction is desired. Since any number multiplied or divided by 1 is still the same number, merely pressing the 1 key followed by the desired $\boxed{+}$ or $\boxed{-}$ key corrects this error:

$$8 \boxed{\times} \text{ (oops, I meant } \boxed{+} \text{)} 1 \boxed{+} 2 \boxed{=} 10$$

It would be worthwhile spending a few minutes inventing and correcting various types of errors so that you will have this information clearly in mind when you need it.

THE DECIMAL POINT

Your hand-held calculator will most likely have a feature called a "floating decimal." If so, the decimal point key will insert a decimal point in a number by pressing it at the proper place during an entry:

$$\boxed{3}\ \boxed{\cdot}\ \boxed{1}\ \boxed{4}\ \boxed{X}\ \boxed{7}\ \boxed{=}\ 21.98$$

The calculator automatically positions the decimal point in the proper place. If you are working with money, just enter the amounts as you think of them. $25 is entered as $\boxed{2}\boxed{5}$; $.19 is entered as $\boxed{\cdot}\boxed{1}\boxed{9}$; $1.95 is entered as $\boxed{1}\boxed{\cdot}\boxed{9}\boxed{5}$. This point is emphasized here for the benefit of those who are accustomed to working with a mechanical adder which requires that the "cents" position must always be filled with an "00." Note how the floating decimal simplifies the following problems:

PROBLEM	MECHANICAL ADDER	ELECTRONIC CALCULATOR
$56.25	5625 + 2200 = 7825	**56.25** $\boxed{+}$ **22** $\boxed{=}$ 78.25
+22.00		
$78.25		
3.14159		
+1.00000	314159 + 100000 = 414159	**3.14159** $\boxed{+}$ 1 $\boxed{=}$ 4.14159
4.14159		

This system has one minor disadvantage, however. Since unnecessary zeros to the right of the decimal point are suppressed, money problems sometimes have answers in which the pennies place or the dimes place is dropped. For instance, in adding $1.35 + $1.45 = $2.80, we have:

$$1.35 \boxed{+} 1.45 \boxed{=} 2.8$$

This is not an error, but it does require that you supply the missing zero.

In many cases, the division of one number by another will result in an answer with an endless decimal fraction. The calculator will show as many places of such a fraction as possible, up to a maximum of seven places. Technically, if the digits dropped from the end of a decimal fraction have a value of 5 or more, the last number retained should be increased by 1. The calculator will not do this, but will merely drop off the excess numbers, introducing a very small error at times. This error is most likely to come to your attention in a problem like:

$$17 \boxed{÷} 3 \boxed{x} 6 \boxed{=} 33.999999$$

Such an answer should obviously be rounded up to the proper whole number. It is interesting to note, however, that if the order of entry of the same factors is changed, the answer is displayed correctly.

$$17 \boxed{x} 6 \boxed{÷} 3 \boxed{=} 34$$

THE MAXIMUM CAPACITY

Most hand-held calculators will accept and display a whole number up to eight digits long, a decimal fraction up to seven digits long, or a mixed number containing eight digits and a decimal point. However, other calculators can handle only six digits while many display 12 or more.

An eight-digit display will report the *length* of an answer up to sixteen digits long, but only the eight left-most digits will be known. For instance, the following is an exact answer:

88888888 ⌷×⌷ **88888888** ⌷=⌷ 7901234409876544

But the calculator will give:

88888888 ⌷×⌷ **88888888** ⌷=⌷ 7901234400000000

Let's think for a moment about the usefulness of this capacity. A number correct to eight significant digits can express the measurement of a mile to within less than 1/1000 of an inch. A number sixteen digits long can express the number of seconds which have elapsed since life first appeared on earth. There are few practical problems which most of you will meet, that really require either larger or more accurate numbers. If you often handle very large or very small numbers, you should be familiar with the method of scientific notation and with the concept of significant places, which are both discussed in the next section.

There are two ways in which you might exceed the capacity of the calculator. An attempt can be made to enter a number containing more than eight digits. This could easily happen, especially if the calculator is being operated by touch. For instance, a certain company has an annual revenue of $108 million and a profit margin of 8.7%. What is their profit?

10800000 ⌷0⌷ ⌷×⌷ **.087** ⌷=⌷ 939600

But this is incorrect! The company actually had a profit of over nine million, not nine hundred thousand. The error came about because we tried to enter a nine digit number. To prevent this kind of error from occurring, the calculator displays an entry overflow signal whenever an attempt is made to enter more than eight digits. A symbol such as $\boxed{\sqsubset}$ appears at the left side of the display, and can be thought of as a hand being held up saying, "Stop! No more numbers." The calculator will operate correctly using the number *actually in the display*, but the warning is there and will remain lit until the $\boxed{c}$ key is operated. The proper way to handle the above problem is to work in thousands of dollars, or even in millions of dollars:

$$108 \boxed{\times} .087 \boxed{=} 9.396$$

The company's profit was $9.396 million, or $9,396,000.

The capacity of the display can also be exceeded when an answer contains more than eight whole-number digits. When this happens, three things occur:

1) The calculation overflow symbol appears at the left side of the display. We shall assume that ours is shaped like a small letter ⌣ .
2) The decimal point shifts eight places to the left of its correct position.
3) The calculator locks up and refuses any further entries or instructions. Only the $\boxed{c}$ key will operate.

Let's do such a problem and learn how to handle it:

$$94328000 \boxed{+} 73529000 \boxed{=} \ \smile \ 1.6785700$$

(Try using some of the number or function keys and notice that they won't work.)

We are told, by the appearance of the ⊔ signal, that the decimal point is eight places to the left of its correct position, and that we must move it eight places to the right. However, it is not necessary to go through the tedious process of counting off eight decimal places. There are eight places in the display, and the decimal point is moved eight places. Therefore we can merely glance at the above answer and see that the decimal point is one place in from the left, and we know that it should be one place *beyond* the end of the displayed number. So we add one zero to the answer. If the decimal point were two places in, we would add two zeros, and so forth.

If you expect to be working with numbers large enough to sometimes overflow the calculator, you may wish to do a few practice problems. Cover the answers given, then check them one at a time as you write out the results from your calculator:

186452 $\boxed{x}$ 377081 $\boxed{=}$ ⊔ 703.07506   70,307,506,000
5999288 $\boxed{x}$ 7123517 $\boxed{=}$ ⊔ 427360.30   42,736,030,000,000
99999999 $\boxed{x}$ 99999999 $\boxed{=}$ ⊔ 99999998.   9,999,999,800,000,000
33333333 $\boxed{x}$ 44444444 $\boxed{=}$ ⊔ 14814814.   1,481,481,400,000,000
5555 $\boxed{x}$ 66666 $\boxed{=}$ ⊔ 3.7032963   370,329,630

MULTIPLICATION AND DIVISION WITH ZERO

The calculator correctly displays the results of multiplication or division with zero.

A number multiplied by zero, that is, a number taken *no* times is obviously zero:

$$25 \boxed{\times} 0 \boxed{=} 0$$

or

$$0 \boxed{\times} 25 \boxed{=} 0$$

In the same way, dividing zero by a number is zero. Nothing divided into 5 parts is still nothing:

$$0 \boxed{\div} 5 \boxed{=} 0$$

On the other hand, dividing *by* zero is called a "forbidden operation" because it can lead to contradictory and meaningless results. For example, we could argue that if $0 \div 5 = 0$, which is an infinitely small number, then the opposite, $5 \div 0$, should be an infinitely large number. Such a number could not be expressed in digits, but at the same time it should overflow the calculator. Try it:

$$5 \boxed{\div} 0 \boxed{=} ?$$

Thus, the appearance of the overflow signal together with a single zero indicates that division by zero was attempted.

NEGATIVE ZERO

What in the world does the phrase "negative zero" mean? Zero sits precisely on the dividing line between the positive and the negative numbers, and therefore cannot be either positive or negative. Yet, perform the following operation:

$$\boxed{-} .00005 \boxed{\div} 1000 \boxed{=} -0.$$

Does this have any meaning? It does not in conventional arithmetic, but it certainly does in calculator arithmetic. The rules that the calculator follows say that any number smaller than .0000001 but larger than −.0000001 shall be called "0." So, for the calculator, zero is not a point, but a *region* on the scale of numbers:

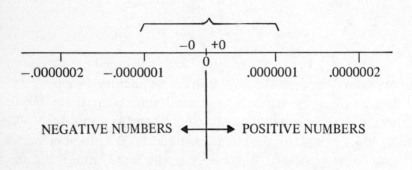

ZERO REGION

Thus, when the calculator displays a result of −0, it is telling us that it cannot give the value of the result, but that it does lie in the left, or negative, part of the zero region.

AUTOMATIC SQUARING

To square a number means to multiply the number by itself, for instance, 33 × 33 = 1089. This operation is usually written in the form, $33^2 = 1089$. The calculator can square a number without the need to enter the number twice. Do both of the following operations and compare the results:

264 ⌷×⌷ 264 ⌷=⌷ 69696
264 ⌷×⌷ ⌷=⌷ 69696

Let's review how the calculator handles multiplication so that we clearly understand why this happens. The first step in any problem is to enter a number into display, for instance a 5:

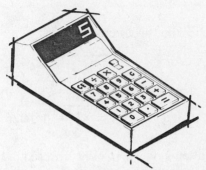

The next step is to enter the *times* instruction:

The entry of the $\boxed{\times}$ instruction caused the 5 to be entered into storage as well as display. The next step would normally be the entry of the second number of the problem into display. But what if we just stop here and press the $\boxed{=}$ key? It appears that the 5 in storage and the 5 in display would be multiplied together, giving a result of 25. And, of course, that is exactly what happens:

$$5 \boxed{\times} \boxed{=} 25$$

Thus we have a rule:

Any number in the calculator can be squared by pressing $\boxed{\times}$ $\boxed{=}$

Try the following problems:

$$35^2 \qquad\quad 35 \;\boxed{\times}\;\boxed{=}\; 1225$$

$$(-17)^2 \qquad \boxed{c}\;\boxed{-}\; 17\;\boxed{\times}\;\boxed{=}\; 289$$

$$1.05^2 \qquad 1.05\;\boxed{\times}\;\boxed{=}\; 1.1025$$

These problems were freshly entered numbers, but the same procedure will work with a result already in the calculator. If the operation is performed in a chain of calculations, pressing the $\boxed{\times}$ key completes the previous calculation, then pressing the $\boxed{=}$ key completes the squaring process. Do the following, and check the display at each step:

$$(7 + 8)^2 \qquad 7\;\boxed{+}\;8\;\boxed{\times}\;\boxed{=}\; 225$$

$$\left(\frac{23}{11}\right)^2 \qquad 23\;\boxed{\div}\;11\;\boxed{\times}\;\boxed{=}\; 4.3719004$$

$$\left(\frac{5 + 8}{2}\right)^2 \qquad 5\;\boxed{+}\;8\;\boxed{\div}\;2\;\boxed{\times}\;\boxed{=}\; 42.25$$

The bracket which appears over the symbols for the two function keys is to make it clear that we are performing an operation different from ordinary multiplication. Thus, when you see the symbol $\boxed{\times}$ $\boxed{=}$ you will know that it has the special meaning: "Square the number in the calculator."

There is no reason why this operation cannot be repeated:

$$25 \boxed{\text{x}}\boxed{=}\boxed{\text{x}}\boxed{=} 390625$$

When this is done, the number is squared twice, or raised to the 4th power. Additional repetitions will raise it to the 8th power, the 16th power, and so forth.

The raising of numbers to other powers is described in Chapter 3, and the general topic of exponents is discussed in Chapter 7.

The calculator will perform a similar operation with a $\boxed{\div}$ instruction, however it is of no value since any number divided by itself is equal to one in every case:

$$15 \boxed{\div}\boxed{=} 1 \qquad\qquad 33 \boxed{\div}\boxed{=} 1$$

The design of the calculator blocks this effect from taking place in addition and subtraction, since it would interfere with the proper handling of negative numbers. It would be of no value to the user in any event, since a number subtracted from itself is always zero. Adding a number to itself can be accomplished just as easily by multiplying by 2.

CHAPTER 2
THE CONSTANT KEY

All our work up to this point has been with the calculator in the CHAIN mode. Let's investigate the CONSTANT mode, and see how the usefulness of the calculator can be greatly extended by a change in its internal programming. If your calculator does not have this feature, you may wish to skip this chapter.

Most users of the calculator will consider the CHAIN mode to be the normal one, and the CONSTANT mode to be a special one for certain applications. You should acquire the habit of checking the position of the CHAIN-CONSTANT switch each time you start to use the calculator. Doing a normal chain calculation with this switch accidently in the CONSTANT position can sometimes produce surprising and inaccurate results.

In the practice examples, we will insert the word CHAIN or CONST before the statement of the problem whenever it is needed to make things clear.

Let's begin by doing a simple multiplication problem, and observing how the internal programming of the calculator differs in these two modes. We'll do the problem, $5 \times 8 = 40$ in both modes, with our imaginary pictures of the calculator set up side by side so we can see the differences:

Chain Mode   **Constant Mode**

Press 5 and 5 is entered into display:

Press ⌷x⌷ and the MULTIPLY instruction is entered:

This has caused the 5 to also be entered into storage. Now press 8.

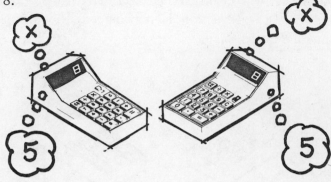

Entering the 8 caused the 8 to replace the 5 in display.

Up to this point the operation of the two modes has been exactly the same. The problem is now fully stated and ready for solution. Press the $\boxed{=}$ key:

Chain Mode   **Constant Mode**

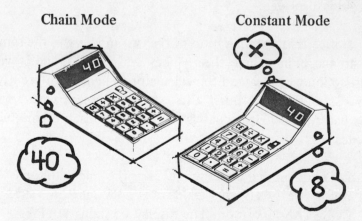

The answer of 40 is sent to display in both cases, but what is left behind in the instructions and in storage is quite different. In the CHAIN mode, the result of 40 was also sent to storage, and the $\boxed{\times}$

instruction was forgotten. In the CONSTANT mode, the 8 that was in display is *transferred to storage,* and the ☒ instruction is remembered. Let's now enter a 6 into display.

In the CHAIN mode, there is no operating instruction. If the ☐= key is pressed, nothing happens. In the CONSTANT mode, the 6 in display is ready to be multiplied by the stored 8. Press ☐= and the result of 48 is displayed.

Notice that the operation of the two modes was the same up to the point where the ☐= key was pressed, and it was that action which caused the calculator to behave differently. You should run through these two sequences with your calculator, visualizing what is happening in each of the two modes.

Let's try another experiment. Clear the calculator and put the CHAIN-CONSTANT switch in the CONSTANT position. The display contains a 0. Press the ☒ key:

The MULTIPLY instruction is retained, and the 0 is sent to storage. Now press **6**:

The 6 is now in display, and the problem of 0 × 6 is set up. Press the = key:

The useless information that $0 \times 6 = 0$ is displayed, *but the 6 has been transferred to storage and the* $\boxed{x}$ *instruction has been retained.* Now press any number you choose, followed by the $\boxed{=}$ key, and it will be multiplied by the 6 in storage. Select another number and press $\boxed{=}$. Again it is multiplied by 6.

In the CONSTANT mode, the entry: $\boxed{x}$ *number* $\boxed{=}$ *will lock the number into memory, and the* $\boxed{x}$ *instruction will be remembered.*

Thereafter, all you need to do is enter a number into display, press the $\boxed{=}$ key, and the entry will be multiplied by the stored constant. Let's try some:

CONST $\boxed{c}$ $\boxed{x}$ 5 $\boxed{=}$ ($\times$ and 5 are locked in)

3 $\boxed{=}$ 15

7 $\boxed{=}$ 35

101.9 $\boxed{=}$ 509.5

$\boxed{c}$ $\boxed{x}$ 2 $\boxed{=}$ ($\times$ and 2 are locked in)

4 $\boxed{=}$ 8

25 $\boxed{=}$ 50

0 $\boxed{=}$ 0 (that is, $0 \times 2 = 0$)

1 $\boxed{=}$ 2 (that is, $1 \times 2 = 2$)

In the CONSTANT mode, the number and instruction locked into storage can be removed by either inserting a new constant, or by operating the $\boxed{c}$ key. Remember that it is the *combination* of the $\boxed{x}$ key and the $\boxed{=}$ key which causes the number to be stored. Although the normal way to put a number into constant storage is the sequence $\boxed{x}$ **number** $\boxed{=}$, it can be put in with the sequence number ⟨×⟩ ⟨=⟩ also. However, this second method will cause the number to be multiplied by itself, and it may be large enough to overflow the calculator, locking it up and making further calculation impossible. It is better to use ⟨×⟩ number ⟨=⟩ when inserting a number into constant storage.

It is possible that, after you have entered a number into constant storage, you may be unsure as to what number is there. It can be brought forward for examination merely by operating 1⟨=⟩. Thus it can be double-checked without disturbing the storage entry.

DIVISION

The calculator will function in a similar manner when the CONSTANT mode is used for division. Let's examine the way the calculator handles the problem of dividing 8, 17, 131, and 14, all by 2:

Operate ⟨÷⟩ key

The $\boxed{÷}$ instruction is entered. Now enter 2:

The 2 is in display. Operate the $\boxed{=}$ key:

This has now set up the calculator with the instruction "divide by 2." Now enter 8, the first number to be divided:

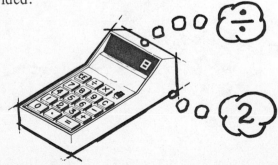

When the $\boxed{=}$ key is operated, the division,
8 $\boxed{÷}$ 2 $\boxed{=}$ 4 takes place. Now continue to enter the
remaining numbers from our problem:

$$17 \boxed{=} 8.5$$
$$131 \boxed{=} 65.5$$
$$14 \boxed{=} 7$$

Thus, the rule for constant division is the same as for
multiplication:

In the CONSTANT mode, the entry: $\boxed{÷}$ *number* $\boxed{=}$
will lock the number into storage, and the $\boxed{÷}$
instruction will be retained.

Here are some practice problems using the CONSTANT
facility for multiplication and division:

A salesman is curious as to what his average weekly
earnings were for each of the last five years, so he must divide
each year's earnings by 52. Insert CONST $\boxed{÷}$ 52 $\boxed{=}$:

$$8735 \boxed{=} 167.98 \text{ (round off to 2 places)}$$
$$9276 \boxed{=} 178.38$$
$$11529 \boxed{=} 221.71$$
$$10657 \boxed{=} 204.94$$
$$12390 \boxed{=} 238.27$$

The local sales tax has just been increased to 8%, and a furniture dealer must re-mark all his price tags with the new sales tax. Enter $\boxed{\times}$ .08 $\boxed{=}$:

199.95 $\boxed{=}$ 16.00 (answers are rounded to 2 places)
349.95 $\boxed{=}$ 28.00
 16.99 $\boxed{=}$ 1.36
 29.95 $\boxed{=}$ 2.40
649.95 $\boxed{=}$ 52.00

A homeowner is shopping for new tile for his 300 square foot basement playroom, and wants the total cost for different kinds of tile. Enter $\boxed{\times}$ **300** $\boxed{=}$:

17¢ per square foot	.17 $\boxed{=}$ 51.00
22½¢ per square foot	.225 $\boxed{=}$ 67.50
29¢ per square foot	.29 $\boxed{=}$ 87.00
44¢ per square foot	.44 $\boxed{=}$ 132.00

MIXED CHAIN AND CONSTANT CALCULATION

When the CHAIN-CONST switch is in the CONST position, chain addition and subtraction can be carried out normally, but as soon as multiplication or division are used in the chain, the first operation of the $\boxed{=}$ key will lock a constant into storage, giving a very misleading result. For instance:

$$2 \boxed{+} 2 \boxed{=} 4 \boxed{\times} 5 \boxed{=} 20 \boxed{+} 2 \boxed{=} 10$$

We know that 20 + 2 is not 10. The calculator has locked in the 5 as a constant, and the erroneous 10 is the product of

2 × 5. The calculator did not make a mistake; we gave it a faulty instruction. However, it is possible to switch from one mode to the other without difficulty.

When you want to use the result of a chain calculation as a constant multiplier or divisor, move the switch to the CONST position, and press ⌐x⌐ ⌐=⌐ or ⌐÷⌐ ⌐=⌐ as desired. This will insert the number which is in display into storage as a constant factor:

CHAIN 2 ⌐+⌐ 4 ⌐x⌐ 8 ⌐=⌐ 48 CONST ⌐x⌐ ⌐=⌐ 2304

Now, operate 1 ⌐=⌐ 48 to verify that 48 has been entered as a constant. (The 2304 which appeared was 48 × 48.)

To get out of the CONSTANT mode while still retaining the number being used in the calculator, you should remember that the calculator will do one more constant operation after the switch is moved to the CHAIN position. To clear out the cons ant factor and the operating instruction, move the switch to CHAIN and perform ⌐x⌐ 1 ⌐=⌐ . This will preserve the number in display.

CHAPTER 3
RECIPROCALS, POWERS, AND ROOTS

A calculator can find the reciprocal of a number almost instantly. It can raise numbers to any whole-number power, and it can find square or higher roots

The ability to find the reciprocal, or inverse, of a number greatly simplifies many ordinary calculations, and every reader is urged to read this description. This procedure, however, requires a calculator with a CONSTANT capability.

RECIPROCALS

To find the reciprocal of a number, operate:

$$CONSTANT \boxed{\div} \boxed{=} \boxed{=}$$

The reciprocal or inverse of a number (sometimes called the multiplicative inverse) is most simply defined as the number, expressed as a fraction, and turned upside down. The reciprocal of 5 is 0.2, because $\frac{5}{1}$ inverted is $\frac{1}{5}$, the fractional equivalent of 0.2. A number, multiplied by its inverse, is always equal to 1. That is, $\frac{1}{5} \times \frac{5}{1} = \frac{5}{5} = 1$. Expressed in decimals, we have $5 \times 0.2 = 1$.

The ability to "turn a fraction upside down" can greatly simplify many calculations, and can often eliminate the need to copy an intermediate result on scratch paper and reenter it into the calculator.

Let's take an example simple enough that it can be worked mentally, so that you can see the process at work. Twelve women and eight men worked on a PTA fair, and raised $800. What was the average amount raised per person? If 20 people raised $800, then their average was $40 apiece. But this was arrived at by a two-step process. First, the number of men and women were added together: $8 + 12 = 20$. Then the receipts of $800 were divided by the number of people: $800 \div 20 = 40$. When these two operations are combined in a single statement they become: $\frac{800}{8+12}$ or, if you prefer: $800 \div (8 + 12)$.

There is no straightforward way to solve this on the calculator. We would first have to add up the number of people, write down the result, then divide 800 by that number.

However, the ability to quickly find the reciprocal solves this problem nicely. Instead of solving it in the form, $\frac{800}{8+12}$ we simply work it "upside down" in the form of $\frac{8+12}{800}$ and then take the reciprocal of the answer; in other words, turn it right side up again:

$$\text{CHAIN 8} \boxed{+} \text{12} \boxed{+} \text{800} \boxed{=} \text{ .025.}$$

Now, .025, which is the same as $\frac{1}{40}$, is the reciprocal of the desired answer of 40. To find this reciprocal, we do:

$$\text{CONST .025} \boxed{\div} \boxed{=} \boxed{=} \text{ 40}$$

Doing this in one continuous sequence, the operation is:

$$\text{CHAIN 8} \boxed{+} \text{12} \boxed{+} \text{800 CONST} \boxed{\div} \boxed{=} \boxed{=} \text{ 40}$$

There is one limitation to this method. The reciprocal of a very large number is a very small number. Since the calculator drops off all digits beyond its capacity, it is possible to lose some truly significant numbers. For example, find:

$$\frac{582,377}{9 + 8}$$

using the reciprocal method. The first part of the operation is:

CHAIN 9 $\boxed{+}$ 8 $\boxed{÷}$ 582377 $\boxed{=}$ 0.0000291

Taking the reciprocal yields:

CONST **0.0000291** $\boxed{÷}$ $\boxed{=}$ $\boxed{=}$ 34364.261

When the two-step process is used, we get:

CHAIN 9 $\boxed{+}$ 8 $\boxed{=}$ 17
582377 $\boxed{÷}$ 17 $\boxed{=}$ 34257.47

It is obvious there is an error somewhere. Three of the significant digits were lost when we pressed the $\boxed{=}$ key to obtain 0.0000291. The two-step process retains the significant digits. Observe now what happens when we try the following alternate method.

CHAIN 9 $\boxed{+}$ 8 CONST $\boxed{÷}$ $\boxed{=}$ $\boxed{=}$
$\boxed{×}$ 582377 $\boxed{=}$ 34257.453

In a problem such as this, the better method would be to add 9 + 8, and insert the sum of 17 into storage as a constant divisor. You will recall that in CONSTANT mode, any number in display can be put into storage by operating ÷ = or x = . In this case we would do:

$$\text{CHAIN } 9 \boxed{+} 8 \boxed{=} 17$$
$$\text{CONST } \boxed{÷} \boxed{=} 582377 \boxed{=} 34257.47$$

Thus, there are three methods of handling the same problem:
  1) The two-step method with or without scratch notes
  2) The reciprocal method
  3) The constant divisor method.

If you often perform computations of this sort, you undoubtedly will want to explore all three, and adopt the one best suited to your taste and the kind of problems you do.

POWERS OF NUMBERS

We've previously pointed out that any number in display can be squared, that is, raised to the second power, by pressing x = . This is true whether the calculator is in the CHAIN mode or the CONSTANT mode

However, when the calculator is in the CONSTANT mode, additional operations of the = key will continue to raise the number to the 3rd, 4th, 5th, ... powers. Each operation of the key increases the exponent by 1.

Put the calculator in CONST. Enter a 2. Press $\boxed{\text{x}}$ $\boxed{=}$. The result is 4. Now continue to press the $\boxed{=}$ key and observe the sequence 8, 16, 32, 64, ... The original 2, which is in storage as a constant multiplier, doubles the display number each time the $\boxed{=}$ key is pressed.

Now enter 3 $\boxed{\text{x}}$ $\boxed{=}$ 9. Again continue to press the $\boxed{=}$ key, and observe the increasing powers of 3.

This procedure applies to both newly entered numbers and to numbers which are in display as the result of a previous calculation:

$$2 \boxed{+} 3 \boxed{\text{x}} 2 \boxed{=} 10$$
$$\text{CONST} \boxed{\text{x}} \boxed{=} 100 \boxed{=} 1000 \boxed{=} 10000$$

Observe that the *first* operation of the key raises the number to the *second* power. If you are raising a number to a high power, you must mentally count the operations of the $\boxed{=}$ key; you should call the first operation of the key "2" and continue to count thereafter. In this way your count corresponds with the power of the number, thus:

Find 5^7:

$$5 \overset{}{\boxed{\text{x}}} \overset{2}{\boxed{=}} \overset{3}{\boxed{=}} \overset{4}{\boxed{=}} \overset{5}{\boxed{=}} \overset{6}{\boxed{=}} \overset{7}{\boxed{=}} 78125$$

However, raising a number to a very high power in this manner can become a little silly. For example, in the section of this book on interest you will find that the computation to find the result of leaving $1.00 on deposit for 25 years, with interest at 5%, compounded quarterly, is 1.0125^{100}. No one, we hope, is going to try to push the $\boxed{=}$ key 100 times.

Fortunately, there is a shortcut. Pressing the $\boxed{=}$ key successively makes the original number increase by the 2nd, 3rd, 4th, 5th, etc., powers. But, pressing the $\boxed{\times}$ $\boxed{=}$ combination makes the number increase by the 2nd, 4th, 8th, 16th, . . . powers.

Any number can be formed by combining certain numbers taken from the 1, 2, 4, 8, 16, 32, . . . sequence. For instance, 100 is the sum of 64, 32, and 4. Seventy-seven is the sum of 64, 8, 4, and 1.

Make a list of all the powers of 2, underline the ones you will need, and go through the $\boxed{\times}$ $\boxed{=}$ process, copying down the values displayed for the numbers you need. As the final step, the values you have copied are *multiplied* together, not added. Let's solve the problem of finding the value of 1.0125 raised to the 100th power:

Operation	Power of Number	Result	
1.0125	1	1.0125	(disregard)
$\boxed{\times}$ $\boxed{=}$	2	1.0251562	(disregard)
$\boxed{\times}$ $\boxed{=}$	4	1.0509452	
$\boxed{\times}$ $\boxed{=}$	8	1.1044858	(disregard)
$\boxed{\times}$ $\boxed{=}$	16	1.2198888	(disregard)
$\boxed{\times}$ $\boxed{=}$	32	1.4881286	
$\boxed{\times}$ $\boxed{=}$	64	2.2145267	

Again, we emphasize that these three numbers must be multiplied together. It was not actually necessary to copy the last number; it is retained in the display, and we perform:

2.2145267 $\boxed{\times}$ 1.4881286 $\boxed{\times}$ 1.0509452 $\boxed{=}$ 3.4633904

Thus, the dollar left on deposit for 25 years has grown to $3.46. This result we computed is in error by only 1/1000 of a cent.

NEGATIVE POWERS

The expression 5^{-4} has the same meaning as:

$$\frac{1}{5^4}.$$

A number raised to a negative power has the same value as the reciprocal of that number raised to the same positive power. A negative power may be computed in either of two ways, with exactly the same result. The first way is to raise the number to the appropriate positive power, and then take its reciprocal by using the CONST $\boxed{\div}\boxed{=}\boxed{=}$ procedure.

However, it can also be computed by using the $\boxed{\div}$ key in the same way that the $\boxed{\times}$ key is used to raise a number to a power. For instance, to find the value of 5^{-4}, the procedure is:

$$\text{CONST 5} \overset{1}{\boxed{\div}} \overset{0}{\boxed{=}} \overset{-1}{\boxed{=}} \overset{-2}{\boxed{=}} \overset{-3}{\boxed{=}} \overset{-4}{\boxed{=}} 0.0016$$

In raising a number to a *positive* power, the $\boxed{=}$ key is operated one *less* time than the power desired. When computing a negative exponent, it is necessary to operate the $\boxed{=}$ key one *more* time than the power desired, because the count starts with the +1 power, next is the 0 power (which is equal to 1 for all numbers) then the −1 power

The correctness of our computation of 5^{-4} can be verified by comparing the results of:

Reciprocal of 0.0016 is .0016 $\boxed{\div}$ $\boxed{=}$ $\boxed{=}$ 625

5^4 is 5 $\boxed{\times}$ $\boxed{=}$ $\boxed{=}$ $\boxed{=}$ 625

FRACTIONAL EXPONENTS

The expression $16^{1/2}$ has the same meaning as $\sqrt[2]{16}$, and the expression $6561^{1/4}$ has the same meaning as $\sqrt[4]{6561}$.

The extraction of roots is covered in the following section.

The computation of fractional exponents such as $2^{3/4}$ is so complex by arithmetic, and so simple by means of logarithms, that their discussion will be found in Appendix I. As a point of information, however, $2^{3/4}$ can also be expressed as $2^{.75}$, or as $\sqrt[4]{2^3}$

FINDING SQUARE ROOTS

To square a number means to multiply the number by itself; the square of 6 is 36, and the square of 9 is 81. Finding the square root of a number is the reverse of the process of squaring it; it is the finding of a quantity which, when multiplied by itself, gives the original number. Thus, the square root of 81 is 9, and the square root of 36 is 6. However, few numbers are perfect squares, with the result that their square roots include a long, usually endless, string of decimals following them.

Calculator arithmetic offers a rapid, easy method of finding square roots which is highly accurate, easier than using logarithms, and virtually error-proof. This method is logical and, once learned, can be recalled in the future with little difficulty, but to remember it you should understand how it works.

When a number is divided by its square root, the result will also be its square root. That is, $64 \div 8 = 8$, and $25 \div 5 = 5$. However, if a number is divided by a quantity *less* than its square root, the result will be *more* than its square root: $81 \div 8 = 10+$. But notice that the true square root lies about halfway between the dividing number and the result, suggesting that we could take these two numbers, add them together and divide by 2 in order to average them, and come very close to the number we are seeking. Let's try it on the calculator.

Assume that we want to calculate the square root of 81. In order to have a starting point, we make a guess that it is 8, so we divide 81 by 8 and obtain 10.125:

$$81 \boxed{\div} 8 \boxed{=} 10.125$$

We now know that the square root of 81 lies about halfway between 8 and 10.125, so we add them and divide by 2. The 10.125 is already in the calculator from the last step, so:

$$10.125 \boxed{+} 8 \boxed{=} 18.125 \text{ and } 18.125 \boxed{\div} 2 \boxed{=} 9.0625$$

Let's clear the calculator, and repeat the same calculation, but without stating all the intermediate answers:

$$81 \boxed{\div} 8 \boxed{+} 8 \boxed{\div} 2 \boxed{=} 9.0625$$

We originally guessed that the square root of 81 was 8. We now have a much improved approximation of 9.0625. The process can be repeated with this new trial divisor:

$$81 \boxed{\div} 9.0625 \boxed{+} 9.0625 \boxed{\div} 2 \boxed{=} 9.0002155$$

We could continue with another step, but we suspect that the result may be 9, so we first verify it on the calculator:

$$9 \boxed{\times} \boxed{=} 81$$

We have been using a trivial example in order to see the method at work, but in a real square root problem the question arises: How do we find a suitable trial divisor with which to start the process? The answer is that *any* number will work, but the steps required can be reduced from 7 or 8 down to usually 3 by a good beginning estimate. This is done as follows:

Write the number on your work sheet, dividing it into pairs of digits, starting at the decimal point and working to the left. You will find that either one or two digits will remain in the left-most position:

2,348	$\sqrt{23\ 48}$
11,834.3	$\sqrt{1\ 18\ 34.3}$
168,329.531	$\sqrt{16\ 83\ 29.531}$

The trial divisor will have one digit for each of the *groups* in the number. This is true even of the first group, in spite of its sometimes containing only one digit.

The first digit in the trial divisor is the largest number whose square can be contained in the first group. Let's work an example to make this clear. Find $\sqrt{780,329}$:

1. Divide the number into groups of two digits. Because there are three groups, there will be three digits in the whole-number part of the root, probably followed by an endless decimal.

$$\sqrt{78\ 03\ 29}$$

2. Find the largest number whose square can be contained in 78. Since 8×8 is 64, which is smaller than 78, and 9×9 is 81, which is larger than 78, then 8 must be the first digit.

$$\overset{\displaystyle 8}{\sqrt{78\ 03\ 29}}$$

3. Fill any remaining spaces with zeros.

$$\overset{\displaystyle 8\quad 0\quad 0}{\sqrt{78\ 03\ 29}}$$

4. Calculate. We are going to divide 780,329 by 800, add 800 to the result, then divide by 2:

    780329 $\boxed{\div}$ 800 $\boxed{+}$ 800 $\boxed{\div}$ 2 $\boxed{=}$ 887.7056

    Drop the decimal fraction from the end and record the result.

    $$\frac{\begin{matrix} 8 & 8 & 7 \\ 8 & 0 & 0 \end{matrix}}{\sqrt{78\ 03\ 29}}$$

5. Repeat the calculation using 887 as the new trial divisor:

    780329 $\boxed{\div}$ 887 $\boxed{+}$ 887 $\boxed{\div}$ 2 $\boxed{=}$ 883.36975

    Again, drop the decimal fraction, record the result

    $$\frac{\begin{matrix} 8 & 8 & 3 \\ 8 & 8 & 7 \\ 8 & 0 & 0 \end{matrix}}{\sqrt{78\ 03\ 29}}$$

6. Repeat the calculation again using 883 as the trial divisor:

    780329 $\boxed{\div}$ 883 $\boxed{+}$ 883 $\boxed{\div}$ 2 $\boxed{=}$ 883.3624

You probably have an answer of sufficient accuracy. Put the calculator in CONSTANT mode and operate $\boxed{x}$ $\boxed{=}$ 780329.12. You have now verified your result. To recover your answer, operate:

$$1 \boxed{=} 883.3624$$

$$
\begin{array}{r}
8 \; 8 \; 3.3624 \\
\overline{8 \; 8 \; 7} \\
\overline{8 \; 0 \; 0} \\
\hline
\sqrt{78 \; 03 \; 29}
\end{array}
$$

Observe that this procedure is virtually mistake-proof. A poor choice of the trial divisor is self-correcting. When the initial trial divisor is very remote from the true root, the error is more than cut in half in the first step, and the correction process becomes increasingly rapid as the trial divisor approaches the correct answer. For instance, if the trial divisor is double the true answer, only one-fourth of this error remains after the next step. If the trial divisor is in error by 10%, only one-twentieth of this error remains one step later.

If a mistake of any sort is made during an intermediate step, it is corrected automatically in succeeding steps. And finally, it is very simple to check an answer by squaring it through the operation of the $\boxed{x}$ $\boxed{=}$ keys.

Let's go through two more problems, step-by-step while you actually work them on your own calculator and maintain your own scratch notes as shown here:

Find the square root of 23,357

1. Divide into groups of two digits.

$$\sqrt{2\ \ 33\ \ 57}$$

2. The largest number whose square can be contained in the first group is 1. ($1^2 = 1$; $2^2 = 4$)

$$\begin{array}{l} \quad 1 \\ \sqrt{2\ \ 33\ \ 57} \end{array}$$

3 Fill the remaining spaces with zeros.

$$\begin{array}{l} \quad 1\ \ \ \ 0\ \ \ \ 0 \\ \sqrt{2\ \ 33\ \ 57} \end{array}$$

4. Calculate:

$$23357 \boxed{\div} 100 \boxed{+} 100 \boxed{\div} 2 \boxed{=} 166.785$$

Drop the decimal fraction and write down the new result.

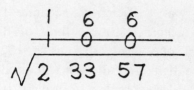

5. Calculate:

$$23357 \boxed{\div} 166 \boxed{+} 166 \boxed{\div} 2 \boxed{=} 153.3524$$

Because there was a large change from the previous answer, we have not arrived yet. Drop the decimal, note the new result, and repeat.

6. Calculate:

$$23357 \boxed{\div} 153 \boxed{+} 153 \boxed{\div} 2 \boxed{=} 152.83006$$

The change from the previous answer was small, so we are probably quite accurate. With the calculator in CONSTANT, press ⌐x⌐ ⌐=⌐ to square for a check, obtaining 23357.027. Then press 1 ⌐=⌐ to recover the answer.

This result was sufficiently accurate for almost any purpose, but if accuracy to the limit of the calculator is desired, perform one more step using 152.8 as the trial divisor. A three-digit trial divisor will produce an answer accurate to six places, and a four-digit trial divisor will produce an answer accurate to eight places. You probably noticed that the intermediate results were always larger than the final answer, so dropping the decimal fractions from the intermediate results not only saves effort, but actually hastens the approach to the final answer.

If your estimating skills are sufficient, a good estimate of the second digit will often eliminate one step, but if finding this second digit requires more than the ten seconds it takes for one step, it is not worth the trouble.

Every square root problem has two answers. The second solution has the same absolute value, but is negative. Notice that $-2 \times -2 = 4$ just as $2 \times 2 = 4$, therefore the square roots of 4 are 2 and -2.

The square root of a negative number is imaginary, and trying to perform $\sqrt{-14}$, for instance, results in obvious nonsense using this method. The proper method is to find the square root of the corresponding positive number, and then show that the result is to be multiplied by i, which is the symbol used for the imaginary number, $\sqrt{-1}$.

The next problem involves finding the square root of a decimal fraction which has no whole number preceding it. The principles and procedures remain the same: As with the whole numbers, we start *at the decimal point*, but this time we work to the right, dividing the number into groups of two digits. The decimal point is brought straight up, as in division. If the first part of the number contains pairs of zeros, we enter *one zero* in the answer for *each pair* in the number. Above the first group, which contains a number other than zero, we enter the largest number whose square is contained in that group, for example:

$$
\begin{array}{cc}
\phantom{\sqrt{}} . \;0\;\;6\;\_ & \phantom{\sqrt{}} . \;9\;\_\;\_ \\
\sqrt{.00\;\;38\;\;62} & \sqrt{.83\;\;12\;\;55} \\[2mm]
\phantom{\sqrt{}} . \;0\;\;0\;\;2 & \phantom{\sqrt{}} . \;3\;\_\;\_ \\
\sqrt{.00\;\;00\;\;05} & \sqrt{.09\;\;38\;\;10}
\end{array}
$$

Let's actually solve one: Find: $\sqrt{.00932}$

1. Divide the number into groups of two digits, starting at the decimal point and working to the right. Bring up the decimal point. Enter a zero over the pair of zeros. Find the largest number whose square is contained in 93, obviously a 9.

$$
\begin{array}{c}
.0\;\;\;9 \\
\sqrt{.00\;\;93\;\;20}
\end{array}
$$

2. Calculate:

.00932 $\boxed{\div}$ .09 $\boxed{+}$ .09 $\boxed{\div}$ 2 $\boxed{=}$ 0.096777

Drop the "777" and record the result.

$$\begin{array}{r} .0 \quad 9 \quad 6 \\ \sqrt{.00\ 93\ 20} \end{array}$$

3. Calculate:

.00932 $\boxed{\div}$ .096 $\boxed{+}$ .096 $\boxed{\div}$ 2 $\boxed{=}$ 0.0965416

Note the result, then operate the $\boxed{\times}$ $\boxed{=}$ keys to square it for a check:

0.0965416 $\boxed{\times}$ $\boxed{=}$ 0.0093202

$$\begin{array}{r} .0 \quad 9 \quad 65416 \\ \sqrt{.00\ 93\ 20} \end{array}$$

Before continuing here is a Reference Summary that will aid you in completing the exercises given below.

Reference Summary:
1. *Divide number into groups of two digits. Start at the decimal point and work to the left for whole numbers; to the right if only a decimal fraction.*

$$\begin{array}{c} 5 \quad 0 \quad 0. \\ \sqrt{26 \ 19 \ 05.} \end{array} \qquad \begin{array}{c} . \ 0 \quad 6 \\ \sqrt{.00 \ 39 \ 28} \end{array}$$

2. *Find largest number whose square is contained in first group. Fill any spaces between this number and the decimal point with zeros.*

3. *Calculate:*

$$261905 \boxed{\div} 500 \boxed{+} 500 \boxed{\div} 2 \boxed{=} 511.905$$

4. *Use result to repeat to desired accuracy.*

Solve the following problems on your calculator and compare your answers with those shown below. Experiment with a very badly chosen trial divisor and see how this process will correct it, usually in no more than five to seven steps. Make an error in an entry and note how glaringly it stands out in the result.

Number $\boxed{\div}$ Trial Divisor $\boxed{+}$ Trial Divisor $\boxed{\div}$ 2 $\boxed{=}$ New Trial Divisor

$\sqrt{67381}$	= 259.58	approximately
$\sqrt{164}$	= 12.8	approximately
$\sqrt{4,000}$	= 63.24555	approximately
$\sqrt{40,000}$	= 200.	exactly
$\sqrt{272.25}$	= 16.5	exactly
$\sqrt{9.8596}$	= 3.14	exactly
$\sqrt{.538}$	= .7335	approximately
$\sqrt{.0087}$	= .0933	approximately

FINDING CUBE AND HIGHER ROOTS

To understand this section, you should have read the preceding section, Finding Square Roots.

The method for cube root is a simple extension of the square root procedure. The steps are:

1) Starting at the decimal point, divide the number into groups of three digits. The left-most group (in the case of a whole number) may contain one, two, or three digits.

2) The trial divisor will have one digit for each of the groups in the number.

3) Find the largest number whose cube can be contained in the first group. Use the calculator to make yourself a list of cubes of 1 through 9. To cube a number, use the procedure.

$$\text{(Constant) } \textbf{Number} \quad \boxed{\times} \; \boxed{=} \; \boxed{=}$$

4) Put a zero in the trial divisor for any remaining groups. Remember, any errors in selecting the trial divisor are self-correcting.

5) When the trial divisor (TD) is obtained, use this calculator procedure:

$$\textbf{Number} \boxed{\div} \textbf{TD} \boxed{\div} \textbf{TD} \boxed{+} \textbf{TD} \boxed{+} \textbf{TD} \boxed{\div} 3 \boxed{=} \text{New TD}$$

6) Using the new trial divisor, repeat the procedure until the desired accuracy is obtained.

Example: Find $\sqrt[3]{318,594}$

Divide into groups of three digits:

$$\sqrt[3]{318 594}$$

Find largest number whose cube is contained in first group:

$$\sqrt[3]{\overset{6}{318} 594}$$

Fill in remaining groups with zeros:

$$\sqrt[3]{\overset{6 0}{318 594}}$$

Perform computation:

318594 ÷ 60 ÷ 60 + 60 + 60 ÷ 3 = 69.499443

Drop decimal fraction and repeat:

318594 ÷ 69 ÷ 69 + 69 + 69 ÷ 3 = 68.305816

Repeat, using 68.3:

318594 ÷ 68.3 ÷ 68.3 + 68.3 + 68.3 ÷ 3 = 68.298713

Make note of result, and cube to check:

(Constant) 68.298713 ⌐×⌐⌐=⌐⌐=⌐ 318593.96

The result is correct to seven significant places.

The procedure used for square roots and cube roots can be extended to higher roots, but beyond cube roots, logarithms may be more convenient. However, the method is presented here for those who might prefer it.

In finding square roots, we divided the number by the trial divisor, added the trial divisor, then divided by 2.

In finding cube roots, we divided the number by the trial divisor *twice*, added the trial divisor *twice*, then divided by 3.

To find the fourth root, we would divide three times, add three times, then divide by 4. However, rather than do these steps over and over, it is easier to compute the terms separately, then combine them. The general formula we have been following is:

When D is an approximation of the nth root of a number, N, then a closer approximation is:

$$\frac{\dfrac{N}{D^{n-1}} + D(n-1)}{n} = \sqrt[n]{N} \text{ approximately}$$

The same formula set up in the calculator notation we have been using is:

$$N \;\boxed{\div}\; D^{n-1} \;\boxed{+}\; D(n-1) \;\boxed{\div}\; n \;\boxed{=}\; \sqrt{N} \text{ approximately}$$

The values of D^{n-1} and of $D(n-1)$ must be first computed separately, and then inserted in the formula. The best brief advice on finding an initial trial divisor, D, is simple trial-and-error, using the calculator.

BASIC ARITHMETIC AND
THE ELECTRONIC CALCULATOR

CHAPTER 4
THE NUMBER SYSTEM

We begin to hear and talk about numbers almost as soon as we begin to speak. Things learned so early in life are often used without being understood. For instance, a child learns that *twelve* is the name for this number of eggs:

Later, when he begins to read, he learns that this word can be written either as *twelve* or as *12*, and he assumes that these are just two different ways of spelling the same word. But there is a world of difference between them. *Twelve* is the English name for this many:

but *12* is a code symbol which means "one ten and two ones."

The number system we use is an ingenious code. Although it was invented in India about 1,000 years ago, it did not come into widespread use until after the time of Columbus. Like much of the knowledge which shook Europe awake after the long sleep of the Dark Ages, it was introduced to the West by the Arabs who had conquered Spain.

To appreciate the beauty of the Indo-Arabic system, imagine the job of having to think up names for a thousand different people. Then make the job more difficult by using only ten letters, and not allowing any name to contain more than three of them. It sounds almost impossible, yet that is exactly what our number system can do. Each number through 999 can be given its own special name, like 329 or 852, using only a ten-symbol "alphabet" and no more than three symbols in each name.

There were two radical ideas which made this system possible. The first of these was to have a numeral which stood for no number of things, and meant no-things – in other words, a zero. The idea of zero may seem obvious to us now, but it surely wasn't to our ancestors. The names we use for the numbers are extremely ancient, many thousands of years old, but the first recorded use of the word "zero" in English occurred only 370 years ago.

The second great idea was making the value of a symbol changeable, depending on its position in the numeral. In the Roman system, the symbol V means this many:

regardless of where it appears in the numeral. But in our modern system, using the numeral 555 as an example, the right-hand 5 stands for this many:

The middle 5 stands for this many:

And the left-hand 5, this many:

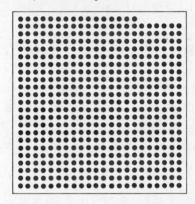

Thus, the same symbol can mean many different quantities, depending on its position in the numeral. The numeral we have just illustrated, 555, means five ones, plus five tens, plus five hundreds. Each time we move a symbol one place to the left, its value is increased tenfold. Because of this positional type of notation, we need the digit named zero. If we want to speak of 5 hundreds plus 4 ones (but no tens), we need a placeholder, the numeral zero serves this purpose. Thus our numeral can be written as 504. If it weren't for the zero, we couldn't tell the difference between the symbols for fifty-four and five hundred four.

Do this with the calculator: Put the CHAIN-CONSTANT switch in the CONSTANT position and enter 1 ✕ 10 ⸗ . Continue to press the = key slowly and say aloud the name of each number as it appears. Each time the key is pressed, the number in the display is multiplied by 10. Now do the same thing with 5 ⌷×⌷ 10 ⌷=⌷ .

This system allows us to express some extremely large numbers in a very small space. The number of pennies in a pile high enough to reach the moon is: 272,415,000,000. Thus, a row of symbols shorter than many people's names can describe an almost unimaginable number of coins.

ADDITION, SUBTRACTION, AND NEGATIVE NUMBERS

The NUMBER LINE is a useful tool in understanding addition and subtraction. A number line is merely a line marked off in equal spaces, with a zero in the middle. Plus numbers are written to the right, and minus numbers are written to the left.

Addition and subtraction can be done by moving back and forth along this line. *Addition is moving to the right.* If you want to add 2 and 5, you start at 2, then move 5 spaces to the right, ending up at the answer of 7.

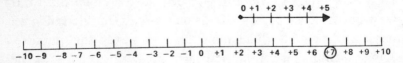

This same problem can be stated a little differently. Here is the diagram for 5 + 2 = 7.

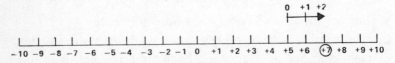

Subtraction is moving to the left. To perform the operation 7 − 3 = 4, we start at 7 and move 3 spaces to the left, ending at 4.

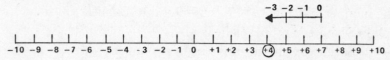

If you have a calculator, you should start using it now. The exercises we are doing are extremely easy, but we are coming to an important idea. These easy problems are needed to explain the idea. Whenever you see an exercise written like this:

$$7 \boxed{+} 5 \boxed{=} 12$$

you should perform it on the calculator. You should then check the calculator answer with the number line answer.

Usually we think of the "minus" sign as being an order, or an instruction. It seems to say: "Here are two numbers. Take one of them away from the other." We are going to ask you to change your thinking. Stop thinking of the minus sign as an instruction. Instead, think of it as being attached to the number. In other words, we are going to have two kinds of numbers:

Positive numbers, like 9, 33, or 528

Negative numbers, like −5 (negative five), −19 (negative nineteen), and −528 (negative five hundred twenty-eight).

We are also going to ask you to stop thinking about addition and subtraction. Instead, we want you to think about *combining* numbers. There are two ways of translating the number statement, "17 − 8 = 9," into English:

1) Seventeen minus eight is nine
2) Seventeen and negative eight are nine.

It sounds as if we have gotten rid of subtraction and instead are adding positive and negative numbers. And that is exactly what we are doing! Let's try an experiment with number lines and with the calculator and see if we can show that this is a useful way to think about "subtraction."

We know that adding two numbers will always give the same answer no matter what order they are added: 5 + 10 = 15, and 10 + 5 = 15. If we have really gotten rid of subtraction, we should be able to do a "subtraction" problem in any order and still get the right answer.

First, we are going to combine positive 9 and negative 4:

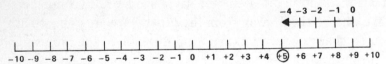

Now make these entries into the calculator:

$$\boxed{+}\ 9 \text{ and } \boxed{-}\ 4 \boxed{=}\ 5$$

The result of the number line and the result of the calculator work are the same, as they should be.

But now comes the step to which we have been building. What is the result of −4 + 9 = ? Let's do it with a number line and with the calculator:

Press the Clear key ($\boxed{c}$) and enter $\boxed{-}$ 4 and $\boxed{+}$ 9 $\boxed{=}$ 5

We have now shown that we can combine −4 and +9 in either order and still get the same answer. We have also shown that it works just as well to forget about subtraction and think only about the addition of positive and negative numbers.

When a number has a negative sign, you are to move to the left on the number line. When it has a positive sign, you are to move to the right. Since most of the numbers we deal with are positive, the "+" sign is usually left off unless it is absolutely necessary. The calculator works like this, too. When you put the first number of a problem into it, it just assumes it is a + number unless you tell it differently by pressing the $\boxed{-}$ key.

Here are some practice problems. Even if the arithmetic is very easy for you, you should still solve each problem using the number line and the calculator, making sure you get the same answer using both methods. The purpose of this exercise is to give you practice using negative numbers.

To combine numbers, using a number line:
1. *Find the first number of the problem on the number line.*
2. *Count off the number of spaces in the second number*
   moving to the right if the number is positive
   moving to the left if the number is negative.

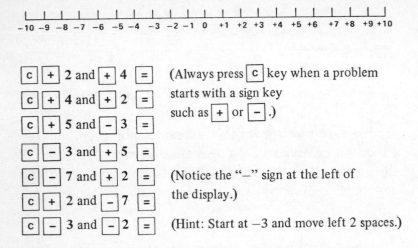

$\boxed{\text{c}}$ $\boxed{+}$ 2 and $\boxed{+}$ 4 $\boxed{=}$ (Always press $\boxed{\text{c}}$ key when a problem

$\boxed{\text{c}}$ $\boxed{+}$ 4 and $\boxed{+}$ 2 $\boxed{=}$ starts with a sign key

$\boxed{\text{c}}$ $\boxed{+}$ 5 and $\boxed{-}$ 3 $\boxed{=}$ such as $\boxed{+}$ or $\boxed{-}$.)

$\boxed{\text{c}}$ $\boxed{-}$ 3 and $\boxed{+}$ 5 $\boxed{=}$

$\boxed{\text{c}}$ $\boxed{-}$ 7 and $\boxed{+}$ 2 $\boxed{=}$ (Notice the "−" sign at the left of

$\boxed{\text{c}}$ $\boxed{+}$ 2 and $\boxed{-}$ 7 $\boxed{=}$ the display.)

$\boxed{\text{c}}$ $\boxed{-}$ 3 and $\boxed{-}$ 2 $\boxed{=}$ (Hint: Start at −3 and move left 2 spaces.)

A cashier making change uses a number line method of subtraction. If you have made a $5.65 purchase and offer a $10 bill, the cashier does not think:

"$10.00
  5.65
$ 4.35

HERE IS YOUR $ 4.35
CHANGE, THANK YOU."

Instead, she starts on the number line at $5.65 and counts money out as she goes towards the $10 you gave her.

Her thoughts are:

"$5.65 PURCHASE,
PLUS 10¢ IS $5.75,
PLUS 25¢ IS $6.00, PLUS
FOUR $1 BILLS IS
$10.00. THANK YOU."

Surprisingly, with this method a cashier can *know* she gave correct change, yet *not know* how much change she gave.

Thinking about money is an excellent way to get a clearer picture of this business of positive and negative numbers. If you have $3 in your pocket, and you owe $5, you are $2 in debt. That is, +3 and −5 = −2. Now, although you are already $2 in debt, you decide to make a new $3 purchase and charge it. You are now $5 in debt because −2 and −3 = −5.

Let's do some more practice with the calculator and the number line, using larger numbers than before. Because counting large numbers along the number line is too much trouble, a drawing of each problem has been made. Compare the drawing carefully with the problem and with the calculator result.

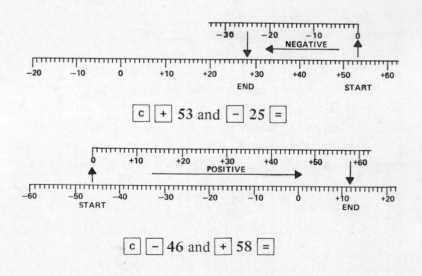

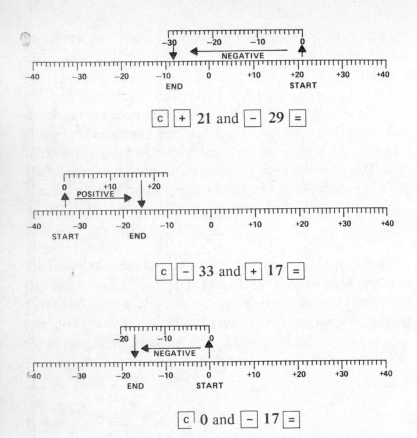

C + 21 and − 29 =

C − 33 and + 17 =

C 0 and − 17 =

When combining negative and positive numbers, we are not limited to just two numbers in each problem. We can combine as many numbers as we like in one continuous operation. In other words, we can keep on going back and forth along the number line as many times as we need to:

C + 19, − 12, − 33, + 128, + 3000, = 3102

PENCIL AND PAPER ARITHMETIC

You should now have a clear understanding of how positive and negative numbers are combined, and how to perform these operations on the calculator. But you won't always have a calculator, and students might not be permitted to use one in school. Almost everyone knows the rules for doing addition and subtraction on paper, so we are not going to repeat them here. However, a great many people find they must work very slowly, else they will make many mistakes doing pencil and paper arithmetic. The calculator can be used as a teaching machine which will very quickly result in the mastery of the different combinations of numbers. This use of the calculator to learn times-tables will be described a little later. Exactly the same methods and principles apply to the learning of the addition and subtraction facts.

Multiplication

Suppose you need to know how many squares are in this diagram:

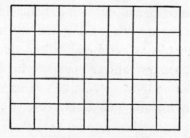

The simplest (but not the easiest!) way to find out would be to count them. The next simplest way would be to count the squares along two edges, and find that the diagram is 7

squares long and 5 squares high. Then we could either add
five 7s together, or add seven 5s:

$$7 + 7 + 7 + 7 + 7 = 35$$

$$5 + 5 + 5 + 5 + 5 + 5 + 5 = 35$$

The easiest way is to multiply, to say, "5 × 7 = 35." But
how do we know that 5 × 7 = 35? The answer is that we
once added it up and memorized the answer. If you said that
5 × 7 = 35, and someone else said, "Prove it," you might
count with 7 fingers and say, "5-10-15-20-25-30-35."

So it appears that multiplication is merely adding the
same number a certain number of times. When two numbers
are multiplied, one of them is the number being added, and
the other is the number of times it is being added. This is the
meaning of the word, "times." When we say, "Six *times*
seven," we mean sevens are being added together *six times*.
And, of course, a *times*-table is merely a list of numbers that
have already been added together a certain number of times.
Take your calculator and put a finger of your left hand on 8
and a finger of your right hand on + . Push first one finger,
then the other, and watch the eight times-table appear on the
calculator display. Do this with several other numbers. If you
have not memorized these lists up to 10 times 10, this is an
easy way to learn them. Try to say each number aloud just

before it appears on the calculator. If you make a mistake, go back to the beginning of that list and start over.

This all sounds very simple, but it is a little hard to believe that when we do a problem like:

$$\begin{array}{r} 429 \\ \times\ 324 \\ \hline \end{array}$$

that we are really taking the number 429 and adding it to itself 324 times. However, we are. Fortunately, the decimal system provides a very happy shortcut. To multiply a number by 10, all we have to do is add a zero to the end of it; to multiply by 100, we add two zeros; to multiply by 1000, we add three zeros. Notice that the number of zeros we add to a number is the same as the number of zeros in the multiplier. For example:

$$34 \times 1\underline{0} = 34\underline{0}$$
$$68 \times 1\underline{00} = 68\underline{00}$$
$$5 \times 1\underline{000} = 5\underline{000}.$$

We can take advantage of this shortcut. Here is 429 × 324, done by using addition and the "added zeros" shortcut, and also done the usual way. Use your calculator to check all the different steps in these two versions of the same problem:

Version 1

$$\begin{array}{rcl} 4 \times 429 \text{ is } 429 + 429 + 429 + 429 & = & 1716 \\ 2\underline{0} \times 429 \text{ is } 429\underline{0} + 429\underline{0} & = & 858\underline{0} \\ 3\underline{00} \times 429 \text{ is } 429\underline{00} + 429\underline{00} + 429\underline{00} & = & \underline{128700} \\ & & 138996 \end{array}$$

Version 2   429
                          X 324
                          ─────
                          1716
                          8580
                         128700
                         ──────
                         138996

The calculator has been designed so that it follows the rules of multiplication whenever the ⌐x⌐ key is pressed between two entries, followed, of course, by the ⌐=⌐ key. Although it relieves us of the dull job of actually performing the multiplication, we should always keep in mind what it is doing and why.

Here are a few practice problems. You might enjoy trying to invent other such problems. The answers have been omitted because we want you to find them yourself.

296296 ⌐x⌐ 3 ⌐=⌐

14593 ⌐x⌐ 846 ⌐=⌐

9739369 ⌐x⌐ 9 ⌐=⌐

32159 ⌐x⌐ 464 ⌐=⌐

15973 ⌐x⌐ 139 ⌐x⌐ 8 ⌐=⌐

How to Memorize Times-Tables

Many children, and not a few adults, are handicapped by a seeming inability to memorize the results of multiplying numbers up to 12 times 12. As a consequence, the simplest problems become painful and tedious, and the results often erroneous. This failure causes a lack of confidence, which then causes further difficulties until finally arithmetic is avoided, hated, or both.

Overcoming this difficulty is relatively simple. However, it requires a clear understanding about the way such information is remembered on the part of both the learner and anyone who may be helping him.

We remember many of the things we know by understanding them — by grasping them with the intelligent part of our minds. For instance, the problem $2 + 3 = 5$ can be solved intelligently because we can instantly visualize the two quantities and count their sum. But trying to remember that $7 \times 8 = 56$ in an intelligent way is useless; there is simply nothing "intelligent" about it. There is no way that it can be attacked by the intellect except through painful finger counting and adding.

However, there is another aspect of our mental apparatus that can be used for this kind of memorization. We have a parrot-like ability to recall sound patterns, a talent that is closely related to our speaking skills. Say the following aloud and observe what happens:

Mary had a little . . .

M I S S I S S I . . .

Notice how the word *lamb* or the letters *P P I* try to burst from your lips automatically and mindlessly. When you say, "Mary had a little lamb," you are not thinking about a small girl named Mary and her pet baby sheep; you are merely rattling off a string of familiar sounds. Once the beginning of the sequence is triggered, the rest comes pouring out thoughtlessly. In the same way, when you say the first three digits of your phone number, the rest comes automatically to your mind.

Arithmetic facts, both multiplication and addition, are also remembered this way. Almost everyone, doing arithmetic, talks gently to himself. Perhaps they actually murmur, or only silently form the words with tongue and lips, but certainly they actuate the sound-pattern memory by starting to say the needed statement. When we look at $4 \times 7 =$, we say the words, "four times seven is. . . " and then we let this parrot-like ability produce the answer, "twenty-eight." Saying something that is not true, like "six times eight is seventy-three," is jarring and discordant, like saying, "Mary had a little goat."

These observations allow us to set down some rules for memorizing times-tables:

1. Times-tables are memorized by saying them aloud, not by trying to grasp them mentally.
2. To be useful, they must be memorized in the form, "five times nine is forty-five," not in the form "9-18-27-36-. . .," which is an entirely separate piece of knowledge.
3. The student must learn to have absolute trust in his sound memory, but he can develop that trust only when he can prove to himself that he is always right.
4. He must make every effort, while learning, to avoid ever saying a wrong statement. If he is not sure, he should not say it, and if an untrue statement is made, the true statement should be repeated several times to erase the memory of the false one.

The calculator makes an ideal teaching machine to help with this task. It is motivating because it is fun to use. It carries no emotional threats, because no one cares what a little machine thinks about him. It builds the student's self-confidence by instantly confirming when he is right.

The first step in using it is to prepare a list of all the multiplication or addition facts with which you always have trouble. Any that cause the slightest difficulty should be written in random order, without the results being shown:

$$7 \times 8 =$$
$$5 \times 9 =$$
$$3 \times 6 = \qquad \text{etc.}$$

Now go through the list. As you press each key on the calculator, *say aloud* the appropriate sound:

5 $\boxed{\text{x}}$ **7** $\boxed{=}$ 35
"Five"   "times"   "seven"   "is thirty-five"

When you are sure you know the answer, you should say it. Now press the $\boxed{=}$ key to prove to yourself that you are right, and to reward yourself with the pleasure of success. If there is any doubt in your mind, you should press the $\boxed{=}$ key first, then say the correct word, and repeat the entire statement several times before going on to the next one.

You should never struggle; this job is not a mental challenge and it does not prove how smart we are. There is a little part of our minds that is like the tiny brain of a parrot, and you should understand that you are training it in the same gentle, patient way you would teach a parrot to say, "Six-times-seven-is-forty-two."

If you are a student, much of this good work might be done during school hours or while doing homework. If it seems appropriate, special permission might be sought from the teacher to allow you to use a written-out times-table in school for a period of a week or two.

Division

Although we haven't mentioned division, much of our discussion of multiplication applies to division, because division is the reverse of multiplication. Division will "un-do" what multiplication does:

$$5 \times 6 = \quad 30$$
$$30 \div 6 = 5$$

But you will recall that we proved that multiplication is actually repeated addition; that the problem of 4×5 could be done:

$$4 + 4 + 4 + 4 + 4 = 20$$
$$5 + 5 + 5 + 5 = 20$$

Subtraction is the opposite of addition. If multiplication is repeated addition, then division should be repeated subtraction. Let's see if we can do division using only subtraction. A simple exercise will allow us to see the principle at work, so let's take 25 divided by 5:

$$
\begin{array}{r}
25 \\
-\ 5 \\
\hline
20 \\
-\ 5 \\
\hline
15 \\
-\ 5 \\
\hline
10 \\
-\ 5 \\
\hline
5 \\
-\ 5 \\
\hline
0
\end{array}
\quad
\begin{array}{l}
(1) \\[1.2em]
(2) \\[1.2em]
(3) \\[1.2em]
(4) \\[1.2em]
(5)
\end{array}
$$

We were able to subtract 5 from 25 five times before we used it up. Therefore we can say that 25 contains five 5s, or that: $25 \div 5 = 5$.

There are two different signs or marks used to show that division should be performed. The basic one is a horizontal bar, with the number to be divided above it, and the divisor below it, such as: $\frac{25}{5}$. This means that 25 is to be divided into five equal parts. Sometimes, as a matter of convenience, the two numbers are written on the same line, with the bar between them slanted so that it is still clear which number is above the line: 25/5 is the same as $\frac{25}{5}$.

This combination of numbers and a division sign is sometimes called a fraction, because it indicates a quantity is to be "fractured," or broken up into pieces.

The other sign for division is the horizontal fraction bar with dots above and below it in place of numbers thus: $\div$. When this is used, the quantity to be divided precedes the symbol, and the divisor follows it: $35 \div 5 = 7$. This is said in English as, "thirty-five divided by five equals seven."

Division is the most tedious of the four basic operations when done with pencil and paper, and it is in division that the speed and accuracy of the calculator is most appreciated. The reason pencil and paper division is so annoying is that we use a shortcut method which takes advantage of the decimal system, but which requires us to estimate or guess. Often the estimate is wrong, and the step must be erased and done again.

An accurate knowledge of the times-tables is necessary if division is to be done quickly and easily. Fortunately, it is not necessary to memorize a whole new set of division combinations. We don't have to learn that 56 ÷ 8 = 7. Instead, the multiplication facts are used. Division is the reverse of multiplication. Thus if we wish to know: 56 ÷ 8 = ?, we can say, "eight times *what* is fifty-six — eight times *seven* is fifty-six." Thus, we have converted a multiplication fact into a division fact.

There is one major difference between multiplication and division: Multiplication always "comes out even." There are no messy little left-over pieces. In other words, when one whole number is multiplied by another whole number, the result is a whole number. But this is not always true of division. For example, let's try to divide 23 by 7, using the subtraction method:

$$
\begin{array}{r}
23 \\
-\ 7 \quad (1) \\
\hline
16 \\
-\ 7 \quad (2) \\
\hline
9 \\
-\ 7 \quad (3) \\
\hline
2
\end{array}
$$

Our answer is that 23 contains three 7s, plus a remainder of 2. There are several different ways to handle this remainder, depending on the purpose of the calculation. Let us suppose we need to answer the question: If a shirt costs $7, how many shirts could you buy with $23? Then the answer is: 3 shirts, with $2 left over. In this case, we would show the problem as being 23 ÷ 7 = 3 R2. The "R2" means "remainder, 2."

On the other hand, look at the following: If 23 apples are to be made into 7 servings of applesauce, how many apples will be in each serving? We now have an entirely different situation. Once the apples are made into applesauce, they can be divided any way we please. In such a case, the answer to our problem would be expressed either as $3\frac{2}{7}$ or as 3.29. These are known as common fractions and decimal fractions, and will be discussed in the next chapter.

We are not going to describe the pencil and paper division procedure. If you do not know it, you will learn it more successfully if it is explained to you by someone as you attempt to work it. However, we have three suggestions for using the calculator to help you practice by yourself so you don't need someone to correct your work:

1. When you are learning, you will want practice problems that "come out even." Multiply two numbers on the calculator; then use the answer and one of the numbers for your division problem. Copy the division problem on a separate sheet of paper so the answer won't be in front of you. When you finish, use the calculator to check the accuracy of your work.

2. The most difficult part of division is estimating how many times the divisor goes into the partial dividend. Use the calculator to help you with this; not as a crutch, but as a learning tool.

3. If you do have an error, use the calculator to check your work to find it quickly. When you've found it, use the time you saved to figure out what error of thinking allowed you to make that mistake.

Is A Number Evenly Divisible By 3?

There is a simple trick which makes it almost as easy to identify a number evenly divisible by 3 as it is to identify odd and even numbers.

Add together the individual digits of the number. If this sum is divisible by 3, then the number itself is divisible by 3.

For example, is 9237 evenly divisible by 3? Add $9 + 2 + 3 + 7 = 21$. We know 21 is evenly divisible by 3, therefore 9237 is evenly divisible by 3.

Is 56 divisible by 3? $5 + 6 = 11$. No.
Is 87 divisible by 3? $8 + 7 = 15$. Yes.

For practice, invent numbers and enter them into the calculator. Use this rule mentally, then check by pressing $\boxed{\div}$ 3 $\boxed{=}$. A number divisible by 3 comes out with no decimal remainder.

Factors and Primes

Recall that an even number is any number divisible by 2 such as 0, 4, −6, 6, ... An odd number is a number not divisible by 2. For example: −1, 1, 3, 251, ... If we multiply two even numbers together, the answer will be even. If we multiply an odd number by an even number, the answer will also be even; and, of course, if we multiply an even number by an odd number, the answer will be even. Use your calculator to satisfy yourself that you cannot find any exception to these rules.

The only way to find a multiplication problem with an odd answer is to multiply two odd numbers together. Again, check this with your calculator.

We can summarize this set of rules:

$$\mathbf{EVEN} \times \mathbf{EVEN} = \text{EVEN}$$
$$\mathbf{EVEN} \times \mathbf{ODD} \ \ = \text{EVEN}$$
$$\mathbf{ODD} \ \ \times \mathbf{EVEN} = \text{EVEN}$$
$$\mathbf{ODD} \ \ \times \mathbf{ODD} \ \ = \text{ODD}$$

This raises an interesting question. We know there are an equal number of odd and even numbers, because for every odd number we can find an even number which is just one higher. But out of the four combinations of odd and even numbers in multiplication, three of them produce even answers. This means that if we took a large collection of numbers picked by chance, mixed them up in a hat, and then pulled them out in pairs and did multiplication problems with them, three-quarters of the answers would be even!

Can we turn this idea around? There are equal quantities of odd and even numbers. But if the answers to most multiplication problems are even, does this mean there are many odd numbers which are *not answers to multiplication problems*?

Yes, it does. To what multiplication problem are the numbers 17, or 23, or 31, or 43 asnswers? None. These numbers are not the result of multiplying other numbers together, but are a new beginning. A number like 24 can be obtained by 2 × 12, or 4 × 6, or 3 × 8. But numbers like 23 or 37 are among the first of a new family of numbers. They

are called *prime numbers*. The definition of a prime number
is this: A prime number is a number which can be divided
only by itself or by 1.

An interesting pattern emerges if all of the numbers are
arranged in six columns. The prime numbers are in bold-faced
type.

I	II	III	IV	V	VI	Remarks
				1	2	
3	4	**5**	6	**7**	8	
9	10	**11**	12	**13**	14	
15	16	**17**	18	**19**	20	
21	22	**23**	24	25*	26	* 5 × 5 = 25
27	28	**29**	30	**31**	32	
33	34	35*	36	**37**	38	* 5 × 7 = 35
39	40	**41**	42	**43**	44	
45	46	**47**	48	49*	50	* 7 × 7 = 49
51	52	**53**	54	55*	56	* 5 × 11 = 55
57	58	**59**	60	**61**	62	
63	64	65*	66	**67**	68	* 5 × 13 = 65
69	70	**71**	72	**73**	74	
75	76	77*	78	**79**	80	* 7 × 11 = 77
81	82	**83**	84	85*	86	* 5 × 17 = 85
87	88	**89**	90	91*	92	* 7 × 13 = 91
93	94	95*	96	**97**	98	* 5 × 19 = 95
99	100	**101**	102	**103**	104	

Notice how the prime numbers (except for 2 and 3) all
fall in columns III or V. Also, note how numbers which are
not prime can be obtained by multiplying prime numbers
together. Why would it be impossible for a prime number to
appear in any of the other columns?

Surprisingly, there is no way to just look at a number and tell if it is a prime number. The only way to find out is to try dividing it by other numbers and see if a number can be found that will divide it with no remainder. The calculator makes this job very easy. Furthermore, it is not necessary to try every number. If a number cannot be divided by 2, it certainly cannot be divided by 4. So it is only necessary to try the prime numbers. Try to find the factors of 323 by dividing it by 2, by 3, by 5, 7, 11, and so forth, using the list of prime numbers you have just been given. This list is long enough to check any number up to 10,000.

It is interesting to try to pick a number that "sounds" as if it might be a prime number, such as 733, then divide it by the primes to see how good your guess is. How far up the list of primes do you have to go to be sure you have checked every possibility? The answer is: Only until the answer in the display is smaller than the divisor you are trying. A more formal answer is that you do not need to test beyond the square root of the number in question.

The *factors* of a number are those numbers which when multiplied together give the original number. Thus, 6 and 8 are factors of 48 and 5 and 7 are factors of 35. Every number which is not a prime number is the result of multiplying prime numbers. That is, $3 \times 5 \times 7 = 105$. Being able to find the prime factors of a number is useful at times, particularly in working with fractions. It allows us to answer questions such as: What number will go evenly into both 91 and 143? If these two numbers are attacked with the calculator by attempting division with the prime numbers, it can be found very quickly that $91 = 7 \times 13$, and that $143 = 11 \times 13$. Therefore 13 will go into both numbers with no remainder.

A number does have factors which are not its prime factors: $4 \times 1\jmath = 60$. However, 4 can be factored into 2×2, and 15 can be factored into 3×5. Thus 4 and 15 are factors of 60, but the prime factors of 60 are 2, 2, 3, 5.

Attempt to factor the following numbers into their prime factors, or state that they are prime. Cover the answers in the right margin, but check each problem as you complete it.

231	3, 7, 11
114	2, 3, 19
210	2, 3, 5, 7
211	prime (why?)
1763	41, 43

CHAPTER 5
NUMBERS LESS THAN ONE

DECIMAL FRACTIONS

We have previously seen that our decimal system can easily represent whole numbers of any size, because the value of the digits changes depending on where they appear in the number. The change of value follows a very simple and orderly system: Each time we move one place to the left, the value of a digit increases tenfold. Thus, the numeral 272 has this meaning:

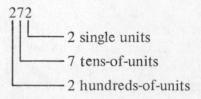

272
- 2 single units
- 7 tens-of-units
- 2 hundreds-of-units

But so far with this system the smallest thing we have been able to talk about is one whole unit. Yet there is a great need to talk about the parts of things. A number system must be able to show ideas like "one-half," or "one-fifth." The decimal system can fill this need in a very logical way. We have just said that numbers increase in value tenfold each time we move one position to the left. This same statement may be made in different words by saying that a digit decreases to one-tenth of its value each time we move it one place to the right, as in:

$$\underline{2},000$$

$$\underline{2}00$$

$$\underline{2}0$$

$$\underline{2}$$

There is no reason why this system of dividing by ten cannot continue to the *right* of the units place. A single thing can certainly be divided into ten parts, or into a hundred parts, or a thousand parts.

We place a decimal point to the right of the ones place to indicate that the additional numbers describe only parts of things. We then continue with the same system, giving us the ability to state the size of a part of one thing to whatever accuracy we desire.

All the rules of arithmetic that apply to whole numbers also apply to decimal fractions. On your calculator, work the following pairs of problems and *write* the first answer in each pair so that you can compare it with the second answer of that pair.

72 ☒ 42 ☐   45 ÷ 3 ☐

.72 ☒ .42 ☐   .45 ÷ 3 ☐

81 ☐ 17 ☐   83 ☐ 19 ☐

.81 ☐ .17 ☐   .83 ☐ .19 ☐

You will notice that the digits in the answers to each pair were the same, and that the only difference was in the placement of the decimal point.

Now take your calculator and enter the problem:

(Constant) 1000 ÷ 10 = 100

Without touching the $\boxed{c}$ key, press the $\boxed{=}$ key. Continue doing this and watch the display; the number 0.0000001 appears. (Note: if the $\boxed{=}$ key is pressed again, 0. will appear. This says that as far as this calculator can tell, the quotient is now zero.) The number 0.0000001 means that something is to be divided into ten million parts. Ten million is very easy to say, but very hard to imagine. If the pages of this book were solidly filled with dots spaced like this:

and if ten million of these dots were printed, it would take more than four books like this one to contain them. Close your eyes for a moment and really try to imagine turning page after page after page solidly filled with dots until you had gone through four books as long as this one.

Now, imagine something cut into ten million pieces. If a mile were cut into ten million pieces, each piece would only be 0.006 of an inch, the thickness of this page.

Just because this is the limit of the calculator doesn't mean it is the limit of the system. The system can easily express numbers down to the smallest thing that exists, and beyond that as far as you wish your imagination to take you.

And, for the few people who need it, there are special ways of using the calculator to express such extremely small numbers.

But let's look at the problem of dividing things into the number of parts we are more likely to need in ordinary life. We'll take this diagram to mean one whole thing:

To show half of something, we divide the whole into ten parts, because that's the basis for the decimal system, and then we take five of those parts, because five is half of ten.

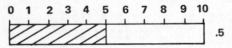

If we wanted to show seven-tenths of something, we would do it like this:

The easiest way to understand the decimal system is to remember that our American money system is also a decimal system, and that whenever we talk about "cents," we are talking about the decimal fractions of a dollar. Although we have nickels and quarters for convenience, the system actually would be a little easier to understand if we used only dimes and pennies.

There are ten dimes to a dollar, so one dime is equal to one-tenth of a dollar. Ten pennies are worth one dime, so a penny is worth a tenth of a dime in exactly the same way a dime is worth a tenth of a dollar. And, of course, it takes ten times ten, or a hundred, pennies to equal one dollar. When we write amounts of money, the first digit after the decimal point is the number of dimes, and the second digit is the number of pennies. Complete the translation of the following amounts of money from numerals to English:

$.22   two dimes and two pennies

$.78   seven dimes and eight pennies

$.35   ___ dimes and ___ pennies

$3.95   three dollars, ___dimes and ___ pennies

$12.35   one ten-dollar bill, two singles, ___ dimes, and ___ pennies.

People who are good at arithmetic seem to have a "feel" for it. The numbers have a real, living meaning to them. Luckily, practically everyone has this "feel" for decimal fractions based on their experience with money. If you want to picture what part of something is represented by the fraction .35, just think of 35¢ worth out of a dollar.

One-half is the simplest of the fractions. It is the result of dividing something into two equal parts and taking one of those parts. One-half is shown in decimal notation as .5 because five is one-half of ten.

Our language has two words to describe the result of cutting something into four equal parts: *a fourth*, and *a quarter*. We will usually use the term, *a fourth*, because it is a little more mathematical, but we want to point out that *a quarter* is also the name of the coin that is worth a fourth of a dollar, or $.25. This makes it easy to remember that these three terms all have the same meaning: a fourth, a quarter, and .25. Let's examine this business of a fourth more carefully. Here is a line one unit long, marked off into ten parts:

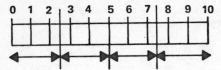

If we now divide it into four equal parts, how many tenths will each part contain?

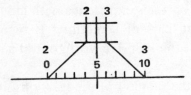

There seems to be no exact answer. Each part contains two and a half tenths. Now, let's magnify one of the tenths that we split in half so that we can see it more accurately.

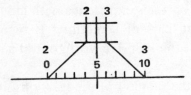

Notice how that tenth was divided into tenths again. If we did this with the whole line, we would have divided the entire line into one hundred parts, because ten times ten is one hundred. And now we can see why a quarter, or a fourth, is represented by .25. Each quarter consists of two-tenths plus five one-hundredths, just as 25¢ consists of two dimes and five pennies.

There is one difference between the notation for money and the notation for other decimal fractions. With money, the pennies place is always filled, even with a zero if there is no other number to go there. But when the decimal system is used for other purposes, any zeros on the end are simply left off, because they don't tell us anything. Although it is true that .50 or .500 or .5000 all mean one-half, there is no reason to show the meaningless zeros, so they are usually dropped. Your calculator does this automatically; add: .25 [+] .25 [=] and note that the answer is given as .5, not as .50.

But things are not quite as rosy with our system as we might like. We frequently divide things into three equal parts, so we need a decimal number for *one-third*. To obtain this we use the calculator to divide one by three:

$$1 \boxed{\div} 3 \boxed{=} 0.3333333$$

Since this fills up the calculator's display, there is good reason to believe that this line of 3s might keep marching on forever. Let's look at a pencil and paper solution to the problem:

```
        .333
 3 /1.000000
   −9
   ──
    10
    −9
    ──
    10
    −9
    ──
    10
```

We don't need to continue. Each time 10 is divided by 3, the answer is 3 with a remainder of 1. The 1 is carried to the next step, and again we have 3 with a remainder of 1. It is quite clear that this fraction would never terminate.

Are there other numbers that do the same thing? Yes, there are, and some of them form interesting and curious patterns. Perform the following on your calculator. Don't try to memorize the results, but do look at them and begin to get acquainted:

$$1 \div 2 =$$
$$1 \div 3 =$$
$$1 \div 4 =$$
$$1 \div 5 =$$
$$1 \div 6 =$$
$$1 \div 7 =$$

Note: The calculator does not have room to show it, but:

$$1 \div 7 = .142857\ 142857\ 142857 \text{ endlessly.}$$

$$1 \div 8 =$$
$$1 \div 9 =$$
$$1 \div 10 =$$
$$1 \div 11 =$$
$$1 \div 12 =$$
$$1 \div 13 =$$

Note: This result is actually .076923 076923. . . endlessly.

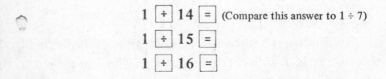

$$1 \div 14 = \quad \text{(Compare this answer to } 1 \div 7)$$
$$1 \div 15 =$$
$$1 \div 16 =$$

$$1 \;\boxed{\div}\; 17 \;\boxed{=}$$

Note: This one has a very long period. It is .0588235294117647... then repeats.

$$1 \;\boxed{\div}\; 18 \;\boxed{=}$$
$$1 \;\boxed{\div}\; 19 \;\boxed{=}$$

Note: This is even longer: .052631578947368421.. then repeats.

$$1 \;\boxed{\div}\; 20 \;\boxed{=}$$
$$1 \;\boxed{\div}\; 21 \;\boxed{=}$$
$$1 \;\boxed{\div}\; 22 \;\boxed{=}$$
$$1 \;\boxed{\div}\; 23 \;\boxed{=}$$
$$1 \;\boxed{\div}\; 24 \;\boxed{=}$$
$$1 \;\boxed{\div}\; 25 \;\boxed{=}$$

Decimal Fractions of Sevenths

A most curious thing happens with the numbers that are the repeating part of the decimal fraction, one-seventh.

Divide one by seven:

$$1 \boxed{\div} 7 \boxed{=} .1428571$$

If we had a calculator with a very large display, we would see that the result of this division would be: 142857 142857 142857. . . repeated endlessly.

On a piece of paper, write the number 142857 in a circle, clockwise:

1
7   4

5   2
8

Now multiply: **142857** $\boxed{\times}$ **2** $\boxed{=}$ and arrange in a circle.

And now: **142857** $\boxed{\times}$ **3** $\boxed{=}$ and arrange in a circle.

Compare these circles carefully, then continue to multiply by successively higher numbers. Don't be discouraged with the result of "times 7." Keep going and observe a very interesting change that takes place.

You can play with this number more easily if you will put the CHAIN-CONSTANT switch in the CONSTANT position, and enter; $\boxed{\times}$ **142857** $\boxed{=}$. Now, merely press any number and the $\boxed{=}$ key, and that number will be multiplied by 142857.

A great many other interesting results can be obtained. Play around, and see what you get.

SIGNIFICANT PLACES AND ROUNDING OFF

We have seen that some division problems have very neat, orderly answers; others have extremely awkward ones. Such results are sometimes like the story of the little girl who read a book on penguins for her first school book report. The report was: This book told me more about penguins than I wanted to know.

In much the same way, the calculator can often give us far more information than we want or need. The questions is: How much do we need? To help answer it, we'll consider the problem of the candy manufacturer whose machine for making peppermint stick turns out long, continuous lengths. The manufacturer finds that seven and a half feet of peppermint stick weighs a half pound. He wants to break this up into twenty-four equal pieces so he can sell a half pound package containing two dozen pieces. How long should each piece be? The problem, then, is to divide seven and a half into twenty-four equal parts. The manufacturer assigns the problem to three different employees. The first, who knows no arithmetic, but may be smarter than all of us, takes a piece of string seven and a half feet long. He doubles it over to obtain two halves; doubles it again to get four fourths; and again to get eight eighths; and finally makes a triple fold in it and has his twenty-four equal lengths.

The second employee translates 7 feet 6 inches into 90 inches, and does:

$$24 \overline{)90.00} \quad 3.75 \text{ inches}$$

The third employee, proud owner of a calculator, does:

7.5 (feet) $\boxed{\div}$ **24** $\boxed{=}$ .3125 (feet)

Here is a drawing showing the value of each digit in the two numerical answers:

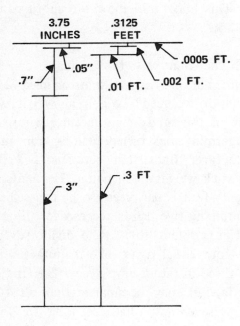

As we can see from this example, the quantities represented by the third or fourth digits to the right of the decimal point are often so small that they have no practical value. Then how do we decide what to keep and what to discard?

It is important to see the difference between two kinds of mathematics. If you are studying arithmetic for its own sake, as an art or science, then every digit is important. But if you are using arithmetic as a practical tool to help get a job done at work or at home, then there is a great deal of difference in the importance of the digits. A gardener does not lay out his plots with a steel rule graduated in sixty-fourths of an inch, and a cook does not weigh out cake ingredients on a chemist's balance. Similarly, we do not carry out calculations about garden plots and cakes to thousandths and ten-thousandths of an inch or an ounce. A scientist, on the other hand, might know that such accuracy is crucial to the work he is doing.

The broad, general rule is this: Don't state numbers with greater accuracy than the usual method of measurement will handle. Then ask, "What is the importance or significance of this measurement"?

For example, when we speak of the weight of an adult, we give the amount in whole pounds, for two reasons. First, ordinary scales might well be a pound or two in error, and second, people's weight varies by a pound or more in their normal living. On the other hand, an incubator baby's weight is watched and reported to the ounce, because not only are the scales more accurate, but the weight is a key sign of the infant's health.

Generally it is assumed that a measurement is accurate only to the nearest unit stated. If a man says his home is on a lot 65 by 100 feet, we would expect that an accurate measurement would show that it was somewhere between 64.5 and 65.5 feet wide, and between 99.5 and 100.5 feet deep. When size is a virtue, the measurement stated is sometimes assumed to be the minimum. For instance, if a friend told you he barbecued a five-pound steak, you would accept that statement as being truthful if the steak were actually somewhere between 4.5 and 5.5 pounds. But when the butcher says that a steak is five pounds, you know it is *at least* five pounds.

However, there are exact rules for reducing an excessively accurate number to usable size. Let's take an example. A gift shop sells candles for $3.35 a dozen. You wish to know the cost of one candle, so you perform this calculation. You should actually do it:

$$3.35 \boxed{\div} 12 \boxed{=} 0.2791666$$

We are now overloaded with information. All we wanted was a simple answer, and here is all this business about ten-thousandths and so forth. What would happen if we just crossed out all the unwanted digits and said that one candle costs $.27? Let's look at a picture of the result we obtained:

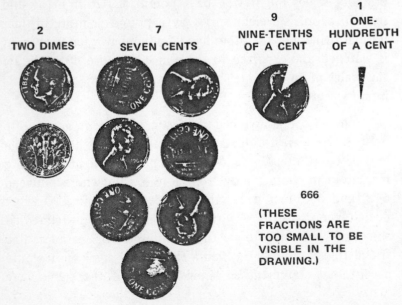

2
TWO DIMES

7
SEVEN CENTS

9
NINE-TENTHS
OF A CENT

1
ONE-
HUNDREDTH
OF A CENT

666
(THESE
FRACTIONS ARE
TOO SMALL TO BE
VISIBLE IN THE
DRAWING.)

It is very clear that an answer of $.28 would be much closer to the truth than the $.27 we first suggested. The nine-tenths of a cent is very close to being a full cent.

So we can now make a rule:

To Round Off a Decimal Fraction:
If the number being dropped is less than five, don't change the preceding number.

Example: .232 becomes .23

If the number being dropped is more than five, increase the preceding number by 1.

Example: .237 becomes .24

We did not give any rule about what should be done when the digit we want to drop is exactly five. Here are the coins for $.025. Should it be called $.02 or $.03?

There is no sound mathematical reason for rounding up to $.03, or rounding down to $.02. Most people use an arbitrary rule that the number should be rounded *up* when the five is dropped. But in practice, other considerations exist. When the choice involves a conflict of interest, the decision goes the way of the party with the most leverage. When the choice is a matter of prudence or safety, the number is rounded the safe way. If you figure you need

3.5 dozen hot dog rolls for a picnic, you'd better round it up
to four dozen. But if you estimate the capacity of a pitcher
as being 3.5 quarts, you should round it down to three
quarts, or you will have lemonade on the floor.

Often there is more than just one undesired digit at the
end of a decimal fraction. The simplest formal rule is to start
at the end and move left, treating each number individually,
then using the result to determine the next step. For
example, round off .37592 to two places:

Step 1. The "2" is dropped, leaving .3759.
Step 2. The "9" causes the "5" to be rounded up,
leaving .376.
Step 3. The "6" causes the "7" to be rounded up,
leaving .38.

With practice, several of these steps are combined, and
the process performed very quickly.

These same rules apply to whole numbers. A man is
thinking about driving from Boston to Miami and seems to
recall that the distance is about 1700 miles, and he wonders
if he could make it in three and a half days, so he does:

$$1700 \boxed{\div} 3.5 \boxed{=} 485.71428$$

The apparent exactness of this answer is meaningless,
because the information which generated it was inexact. Not
only should the decimal be dropped, but the whole number
should be rounded to 500 miles. The final statement is: If it's
about 1700 miles to Miami, you have to drive about
500 miles a day to make it in three and a half days.

When a number is rounded off, the zeros are usually still necessary to show the size of the number. We cannot round 528 to "5"; we must still call it "500." The zeros suggest that we don't know what exact value goes in those places. The digits that have *meaning*, or significance are called *significant* digits, so distinguish them from the zeros that are merely being used as placeholders in the decimal system.

When dealing with approximate numbers, the rule is: An answer cannot have more significant digits than the *least accurate* number which helped produce it. This still leaves a few questions unanswered, such as: How do we indicate that the *Indianapolis 500* is a race of exactly 500 miles?

Here are some practice problems in rounding off. Solving them is important to fully understanding this discussion. Cover the answers in the right margin, perform each calculation on the calculator, copy the answer on paper, then round it off as required. Check each solution against the given answer, and determine the reason for any error before proceeding with the next problem. Assume that all zeros at the end of whole numbers and at the beginning of decimal fractions are not significant. Round each answer to the number of significant places in the least accurate of the two numbers:

$$45.123 \times 850 = \qquad 38,000$$
$$.006 \times 38 = \qquad .2$$
$$.389 \times 70 = \qquad 30$$

$$7.61 \times 428 = \qquad 3250$$
$$3200 \times 7.1 = \qquad 23{,}000$$
$$8656 \div 3.771 = \qquad 2295$$
$$8.08 \times .329 = \qquad 2.66$$
$$.003 \div 1.5281 = \qquad .002$$

COMMON FRACTIONS

We have seen how the calculator and the decimal system handle numbers which represent parts of things, and that a statement concerning part of something could be translated into decimal numbers by simple division:

One-fourth means $1 \div 4 = .25$

Up to this point, the symbol we have used for division has been this: $\boxed{\div}$. However, there is another symbol used to mean division. It consists of a horizontal line, with the number that is to be divided above the line, and the divisor (divider) written below the line. With this system, the fraction, one-fourth, is written: $\frac{1}{4}$ and has exactly the same meaning as $1 \div 4$.

The difference between these two methods of showing division is largely a matter of custom, however they have slightly different uses. Generally the form, $1 \div 4$, means that the division is to be performed immediately, but $\frac{1}{4}$ can be left in that form, to stand for the number, one-fourth. The form, $\frac{1}{4}$ is called a *common fraction* to distinguish it from the form, .25, which is called a *decimal fraction*.

There is a tendency for long-established trades and skills, such as carpentry, to use common fractions, and for newer, more advanced skills, such as machine work, to use decimal fractions.

Because the two distinct numerals in a common fraction must be talked about individually, each has a name. The numeral above the line is called the *numerator*, and the one below the line is called the *denominator*.

There is an easy trick to remembering which is which. When the word *numerator* is said aloud, the beginning *nume* sound is thin and high-pitched. The beginning sound of *denom*inator is low-pitched and comes from the throat. This provides the key to remembering:

$$\frac{\text{numerator (high)}}{\text{denominator (low)}}$$

Common fractions have a major disadvantage. Because they are composed of two separate, but related, numerals, designing calculators or computers to accept or display them in common fraction form would be expensive, and wasteful of time, space, and calculating ability.

Converting a decimal fraction to a common fraction is done very easily. The numerator is formed from the digits of the decimal fraction, and the denominator is a 1, followed by as many zeros as there are digits in the numerator:

$$.28 = \frac{28}{100} \qquad .486 = \frac{486}{1000} \qquad .3 = \frac{3}{10}$$

The main value of the common fraction form is to serve as a tool, and as an intermediate step in calculations. Word statements about the parts of things can be put into common fraction form without any additional calculation. The quantity, one-fourth, is represented by $\frac{1}{4}$; and the quantity, seven-sixteenths, is represented by $\frac{7}{16}$. The rule being used is easy to see: The first number word goes above the bar, and the second word − the one with the "th" on the end − goes below the bar.

The common fraction form is widely used in formulas in order to show that division should be performed. For instance, because there are 12 inches in a foot, a length expressed in inches must be divided by 12 to convert it to feet. A very compact way to say this is:

$$feet = \frac{inches}{12}$$

A complete mastery of numerical common fractions is essential as groundwork for algebra and higher mathematics, and a student should not be misled into thinking they can be ignored. This book, however, is confined to arithmetic, with an emphasis on calculator arithmetic. Therefore, we offer only a summary of the rules for handling fractions. These you may skip if you are familiar with them. The rules are followed by a complete explanation of entering common fraction statements and formulas into the calculator.

Summary of Rules for Common Fractions

1. The numerator and denominator can be multiplied or divided by the same number without changing the value of the fraction. Thus:

$$\frac{1}{2}, \frac{2}{4}, \text{ and } \frac{5}{10}$$

all have the same value:

$$\frac{1}{2} \times \frac{2}{2} = \frac{2}{4} \qquad \frac{5 \div 5}{10 \div 5} = \frac{1}{2}$$

2. Fractions must have the same denominator before they can be added or subtracted. If they do not, one or both must be changed in accordance with Rule 1.

3. When fractions are added, only the numerators are added; and the answer placed over the common denominator:

$$\frac{2}{7} + \frac{3}{7} = \frac{5}{7}$$

4. When fractions are subtracted, only the numerators are subtracted; and the answer placed over the common denominator:

$$\frac{5}{7} - \frac{3}{7} = \frac{2}{7}$$

5. *When fractions are multiplied, the numerators are multiplied together to obtain the new numerator, and the denominators are multiplied to obtain the new denominator:*

$$\frac{3}{4} \times \frac{5}{8} = \frac{15}{32}$$

6. *When fractions are divided, the divisor, which is the second of the two fractions, is inverted, and multiplication is performed:*

$$\frac{1}{2} \div \frac{5}{8} = \frac{1}{2} \times \frac{8}{5} = \frac{8}{10}$$

7. *If the numerator and denominator are the same, the fraction has a value of 1, and should be so stated:*

$$\frac{5}{5} = 1 \qquad \frac{19}{19} = 1$$

8. *If the numerator is larger than the denominator, the fraction should be changed to a mixed number in the final answer. Perform the indicated division, stating the remainder in fraction form:*

$$\frac{77}{8} = \qquad 8\overline{)77}^{\,9\frac{5}{8}}$$

9. *To convert a mixed number to a fraction, multiply the whole number by the denominator and add the numerator to the result, which is then placed over the original denominator:*

$$9 \tfrac{5}{8} : \ 8 \times 9 = 72, + 5 = 77$$

Thus:

$$9 \tfrac{5}{8} = \frac{77}{8}$$

10. *To add mixed numbers, first add the fractions. If this result is an improper fraction, reduce to a mixed number, and add the whole-number portion to the existing whole numbers:*

Step 1		**Step 2**	
	$11 \tfrac{3}{5}$		11
	$+ \ 5 \tfrac{4}{5}$		5
	$\tfrac{7}{5} = 1 \tfrac{2}{5} \rightarrow$		$+ \ 1 \tfrac{2}{5}$
			$17 \tfrac{2}{5}$

11. *To subtract mixed numbers, first subtract the fractions. If this is not possible, subtract 1 from the whole number, convert it to a fraction (such as $\tfrac{3}{3}$, $\tfrac{8}{8}$, etc.) and add it to the existing fraction, then continue:*

Step 1		**Step 2**	
	$17 \tfrac{2}{5}$		$\overset{6}{1\cancel{7}} \tfrac{7}{5}$
	$- \ 5 \tfrac{4}{5}$		$- \ 5 \tfrac{4}{5}$
			$11 \tfrac{3}{5}$

12. In the addition and subtraction of mixed numbers, the fractions must have the same denominators. If they do not, handle as in Rules 1 and 2.

13. To multiply a whole number by a fraction, give the whole number a denominator of 1, and proceed as in Rule 5:

$$23 \times \frac{3}{4} = \frac{23}{1} \times \frac{3}{4} = \frac{69}{4} = 17\tfrac{1}{4}$$

14. To multiply a mixed number by a fraction, choose the easier method:
    Convert the mixed number to an improper fraction and proceed as in Rule 5.
    Multiply the whole number by the fraction as in Rule 13, and multiply the fraction by the fraction as in Rule 5. Add the final results.

15. To multiply two mixed numbers, convert them into improper fractions as in Rule 9, and multiply as in Rule 5.

16. For division involving whole numbers and/or fractions, set up the problem as in Rules 13, 14, and 15. As the last step before solving, invert the divisor as in Rule 6.

17. To simplify compound fractions, that is, fractions which have another fraction in the numerator and/or denominator, treat the central fraction bar as a division sign, and proceed as in the division of fractions:

$$\frac{\frac{1}{2}}{\frac{3}{4}} = \frac{1}{2} \div \frac{3}{4} = \frac{1}{2} \times \frac{4}{3} = \frac{4}{6} = \frac{2}{3}$$

In reviewing this very complex set of rules, it is easy to see why designers of computers and calculators prefer to use the decimal fraction system.

There are three basically different ways to use the calculator in working with statements containing common fractions. Each way has its advantages and disadvantages, and the user familiar with all of them can choose the one which is easiest for each particular job.

The first way is to keep the work in common fraction form, using the calculator to help with the more complicated intermediate steps. If the problem is fairly simple, and if the results are required to be in common fraction form, this is the best approach. There is no need to describe this, since it consists of separate, basic calculations. However, there is one trick of possible value. Suppose you have to add several mixed numbers all with the *same* denominator, as might happen in carpentry work:

$$7\ 3/8$$
$$5\ 5/8$$
$$+11\ 1/8$$

The calculator can add two entirely separate sets of numbers at the same time, provided some zeros are maintained between the two sets. The above problem could be entered this way:

$$
\begin{array}{r}
7003 \\
5005 \\
+11001 \\
\hline
23009
\end{array}
$$

Thus, the answer to the problem is 23 9/8, or 24 1/8. Just be careful; there are several chances for errors.

The second approach to common fractions is to use the calculator to individually convert each common fraction into its decimal equivalent and write each answer. Then the calculator is used to solve the decimal problem. Although it is sometimes necessary to write some intermediate answers, this method is usually wasteful and time-consuming.

The third approach is to use the maximum capability of the calculator, treating each common fraction as a division statement, if possible, and obtaining a result with as few intermediate notes as possible. The final answer will be in decimal form.

Addition of Fractions

If the fractions all have the same denominator, add the numerators on the calculator, then divide the sum by the denominator:

$$3/8 + 5/8 + 2/8 + 7/8 =$$

3 $\boxed{+}$ 5 $\boxed{+}$ 2 $\boxed{+}$ 7 $\boxed{\div}$ 8 $\boxed{=}$ 2.125

If the fractions have different denominators, the division indicated by the fraction can be performed, a written note made of the result, then the same thing done with the next fraction, and so forth. Finally, all these numbers can be added. Notice that you never have to write the last answer; just leave it in the calculator as the first number to be added.

However, there is a clever trick which makes it possible to add the fractions directly. Let's take this problem:

$$\frac{3}{16} + \frac{4}{9} =$$

This problem says:
1. Divide 3 by 16   3 $\boxed{\div}$ 16 $\boxed{=}$ .1875
2. Divide 4 by 9   4 $\boxed{\div}$ 9 $\boxed{=}$ .4444444
3. Add the answers of 1 and 2   .4444444 $\boxed{+}$ .1875 $\boxed{=}$ .6319444

What would happen if we just went ahead and entered the problem into the calculator as it is written? That is,

$$3 \boxed{\div} 16 \boxed{+} 4 \boxed{\div} 9 \boxed{=} .4652777$$

The answer is wrong, and for a good reason. The last step in the procedure, the $\boxed{\div}$ 9 step, divided *everything* preceding it by 9, and we only wanted to divide the 4 by the 9. The answer obtained was: $\frac{3}{16} \div 9$, plus $4 \div 9$!

There is no way we can avoid that faulty division of: $\frac{3}{16}$ by 9, because the calculator performs each step on the answer to all the preceding steps. But we can compensate for the faulty division by doing an equal and opposite faulty multiplication.

If we perform the first step, 3 ÷ 16, and then multiply this by 9, that answer will be 9 times too large. We add the "4" of the $\frac{4}{9}$ to this. Then when we divide by 9, we do two things: We divide the 4 by the 9, just as we wanted to, and also recover the correct answer to 3 ÷ 16.

Let's try it:

$$3 \boxed{\div} 16 \boxed{\times} 9 \boxed{+} 4 \boxed{\div} 9 \boxed{=} .6319444$$

You should reread this carefully, perhaps checking each individual statement on your calculator, until you are sure you understand the reasoning. The rule is:

*To add a fraction to **any** number you go:*

$\boxed{\times}$ *Denominator* $\boxed{+}$ *Numerator* $\boxed{\div}$ *Denominator*

Let's set out a three-part addition problem, with the calculator procedure underneath it so the steps are visible:

$$\frac{5}{8} \quad + \quad \frac{3}{4} \quad + \quad \frac{7}{16}$$

$$\underbrace{5 \boxed{\div} 8} \quad \underbrace{\boxed{\times} 4 \boxed{+} 3 \boxed{\div} 4} \quad \underbrace{\boxed{\times} 16 \boxed{+} 7 \boxed{\div} 16} = 1.8125$$

Here are four practice problems with the answers given in the right margin. Check the answer to each problem as you complete it.

$$\tfrac{2}{7} + \tfrac{1}{5} + \tfrac{5}{16} = \qquad .7982141$$

$$\tfrac{5}{21} + \tfrac{11}{17} + \tfrac{1}{3} = \qquad 1.2184873$$

$$\tfrac{3}{8} + 1 + \tfrac{5}{11} = \qquad 1.8295454$$

$$\tfrac{3}{8} + 1\tfrac{5}{11} = \qquad 1.8295454$$

Addition of Mixed Numbers

If you found the correct answers to the last two problems, you already know the answer to this topic. The *whole-number part* of any mixed number is added to the preceding result (or merely entered, if it is the first term in a problem), and then the special ⌐×⌐ D ⌐+⌐ N ⌐+⌐ D procedure is begun, for example:

$$3\tfrac{5}{8} + 2\tfrac{1}{3} = ?$$

$$3 \quad + \quad \frac{5}{8} \qquad + 2 \quad + \quad \frac{1}{3}$$

3   ⌐×⌐8⌐+⌐5⌐÷⌐8   ⌐+⌐2   ⌐×⌐3⌐+⌐1⌐÷⌐3 ⌐=⌐5.9583333

Try several more mixed-number problems:

$$3\tfrac{1}{2} + 2\tfrac{3}{8} + 5\tfrac{1}{4} = \qquad 11.125$$

$$117\tfrac{3}{32} + 9\tfrac{5}{7} + 83\tfrac{11}{17} = \qquad 210.45508$$

$$5\tfrac{3}{17} + 8\tfrac{15}{19} + 11\tfrac{13}{23} = \qquad 25.53116$$

You might find it interesting to do this last problem with pencil and paper and time yourself. Because the denominators are all prime numbers, the lowest common denominator is found by multiplying them all together.

Subtraction of Fractions

The principle explained for the addition of fractions applies equally well to the subtraction of fractions, the only difference being that the "+" sign is changed to a "−" sign.

Subtract: $\frac{5}{8} - \frac{3}{16}$

$$5 \boxed{\div} 8 \boxed{\times} 16 \boxed{-} 3 \boxed{\div} 16 \boxed{=} .4375$$

Subtraction of Mixed Numbers

Let's go a little slowly here. The number $2\frac{3}{4}$ can also be expressed as $2 + \frac{3}{4}$. When we try to do the problem $5 - 2\frac{3}{4}$ using our shortcut method, we know we have to separate the "2" from the "$\frac{3}{4}$", but do we think of it as $5 - 2 + \frac{3}{4}$, or do we think of $5 - 2 - \frac{3}{4}$? A few moments thought clears up the matter. We want to take *both* the 2 and the $\frac{3}{4}$ away from the 5, so both should have a negative sign. This problem is set up as:

$$5 \boxed{-} 2 \boxed{\times} 4 \boxed{-} 3 \boxed{\div} 4 \boxed{=} 2.25$$

Here are five practice problems in the addition and subtraction of fractions, whole numbers, and mixed numbers. The answers are given at the right and should be checked after each problem and the cause for any errors found.

For reference, here are the two shortcut procedures:

To add a fraction:

$\boxed{\times}$ Denominator $\boxed{+}$ Numerator $\boxed{\div}$ Denominator

To subtract a fraction:

$\boxed{\times}$ Denominator $\boxed{-}$ Numerator $\boxed{\div}$ Denominator

$$15 + 3\tfrac{3}{8} - 5\tfrac{1}{2} + 17 = 29.875$$
$$\tfrac{3}{16} + \tfrac{7}{16} + \tfrac{11}{16} + \tfrac{5}{16} = 1\tfrac{10}{16} \text{ or } 1\tfrac{5}{8} \text{ or } 1.625$$

(Did you merely add the numerators?)

$$\tfrac{88}{17} + \tfrac{1}{173} + \tfrac{5}{211} + \tfrac{6}{7} = 6.0630901$$
$$1\tfrac{3}{4} + 2\tfrac{1}{2} - 7\tfrac{3}{4} + 3\tfrac{1}{2} = \text{Answer is } 0$$

(Did you convert these simple fractions mentally?)

$$8\tfrac{11}{16} + 5\tfrac{3}{8} - 1\tfrac{1}{16} = 13$$

Multiplication of Common Fractions

This operation involves several new ideas, so we want to review a few basic principles to build upon.

Usually we think that "to multiply" means "to make larger," but this is not always true. Sometimes the answer to a multiplication problem can be smaller than the number being multiplied. How can this happen? Let's imagine walking, step by step, along the five times-table:

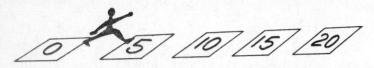

At each step, the number increases by 5, so that after two steps, we are at 10; after three steps, we are at 15. Now, what would happen if we took two and a half steps?

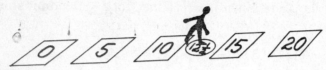

Obviously, we would be halfway between 10 and 15, or at $12 \frac{1}{2}$. But now let's look carefully at the first step. If we can take a half-step at other places, why can't we start out with a half-step?

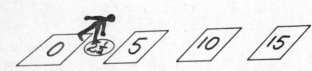

We certainly can, and in this case we did. In exactly the same way that multiplication is done, we took a half-step along the five times-table and arrived at $2 \frac{1}{2}$. Just as this statement is true: $3 \times 5 = 15$, so this statement is true also: $\frac{1}{2} \times 5 = 2 \frac{1}{2}$.

The answer we obtained is the answer to the question: What is one-half *of* five? So, we want to stop for a moment and talk about that little word, *of*. You know that certain English words can be translated directly into mathematical terms or symbols. For instance:

and means *plus:* 2 *and* 3 are 5,
$$2 + 3 = 5$$
are (or is) means *equals:* 2 and 3 *are* 5,
$$2 + 3 = 5$$

Of means *times*. When the word *of* occurs in a fraction problem or a percent problem, you should substitute the word "times" or the symbol ✕. If you did not already understand this clearly, would you look at the ceiling and repeat "*Of* means *times*" until you are sure you will never forget it.

Now, to return to our steps along the five times-table, we saw that if we started with a half-step instead of a whole one, we would arrive at $2\frac{1}{2}$. But there is no reason why it must be a half-step. It could be a one-fifth step, which would take us to 1, or it could be *any* size part-step, and we could arrive at any point we wished between 0 and 5. And in any of those part-steps, we would be performing multiplication, and getting an answer smaller than the number we multiplied.

Whenever a number is multiplied by a proper fraction, the answer is smaller than the number being multiplied. And this is true whether it is a common fraction or a decimal fraction.

We've gone through the business of walking along the five times-table, step-by-step. We're now going to do the same thing with something we have called "the one-half times-table." The one-half times-table is formed like any other times-table: $\frac{1}{2}$, 1, $1\frac{1}{2}$, 2, $2\frac{1}{2}$, 3.

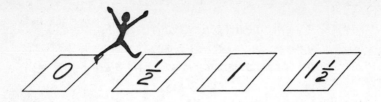

Again, let's look at that important space between 0 and $\frac{1}{2}$. And again, there is no reason why we have to take a full step. We could take a half-step, and we could show this in numerals as: $\frac{1}{2}$ X $\frac{1}{2}$

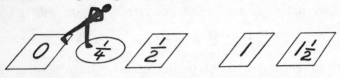

It is clear that the statement: $\frac{1}{2}$ X $\frac{1}{2}$ = $\frac{1}{4}$ is true. And when the same statement is made in decimal terms, the reason for its truth is equally clear: .5 X .5 = .25

Using the calculator to multiply fractions is simple and straightforward. Let's set up such a problem in three different notations, remembering that the fraction bar means to divide:

$$\frac{1}{2} \times \frac{3}{4} \times \frac{5}{6} =$$

$$1/2 \times 3/4 \times 5/6 =$$

1 $\div$ 2 $\boxed{\times}$ 3 $\div$ 4 $\boxed{\times}$ 5 $\div$ 6 $\boxed{=}$ .3125

The rule is very clear. Start by entering a numerator. Then put a ÷ sign in front of every denominator and a X sign in front of every numerator. Just so this basic rule is followed, the numbers may be entered in any order. Try entering all the numerators with their X signs first, then all the denominators with their ÷ signs.

However, be very careful about that first step! If you are beginning a new chain calculation, do not put a × sign in front of the *first* numerator, or you will lose it. You are telling the calculator to multiply it by the zero in the calculator, and any number times zero is zero. On the other hand, if you are tacking a fraction multiplication onto a previous problem in the calculator, you do need the × sign so the calculator will know what to do with the new entry. Here are some practice problems in the multiplication of fractions. Check the answer in the right margin after each problem:

Enter first numerator, then go:

$\boxed{\div}$ *Denominator* $\boxed{\times}$ *Numerator*

$$\frac{3}{8} \times \frac{7}{16} \times \frac{5}{11} = .0745738$$

$$\frac{1}{2} \times \frac{19}{20} \times \frac{11}{32} = .1632812$$

$$\frac{7}{16} \times \frac{3}{5} \times 8 = 2.1$$

$$\frac{25}{5} \times \frac{1}{7} \times \frac{71}{19} = 2.6691728$$

$$\frac{5}{3} \times \frac{12}{113} \times \frac{71}{4} = 3.141592$$

Note: There may be minor differences in answers depending on the order in which terms are entered.

Division of Fractions

The rule for dividing by a fraction using pencil and paper is to invert the divisor and multiply:

$$\frac{1}{2} \div \frac{3}{4} = \frac{1}{2} \times \frac{4}{3} = \frac{4}{6}$$

This same rule can be followed performing division on the calculator, but there is really no reason to go to the trouble of rewriting the problem when the principle to be followed is so easy to remember. Since division is the opposite of multiplication, whenever we see the ÷ sign, we do the opposite. With multiplication, we multiply by the numerator and divide by the denominator. With division, we divide by the numerator and multiply by the denominator:

$$\frac{5}{16} \div \frac{3}{8} =$$

5 ÷ 16 ÷ 3 × 8 = .8333328

Here are some practice problems, with the answers given as usual. Note that division and multiplication can be intermixed:

$$\frac{5}{11} \div \frac{3}{4} = \qquad .6060604$$

$$\frac{2}{3} \div \frac{2}{3} = \qquad .9999999$$

$$\frac{11}{15} \times \frac{1}{2} \div \frac{7}{8} = \qquad .4190472$$

$$\frac{19}{32} \div \frac{3}{8} \times \frac{4}{9} = \qquad .7037034$$

$$\frac{7}{16} \div \frac{1}{2} \div \frac{3}{4} = \qquad 1.1666664$$

Multiplication and Division of Mixed Numbers

It would be very nice if the calculator could handle a problem such as $3\frac{1}{2} \times 5\frac{3}{4}$ without having to go through any intermediate steps. It can't, at least not without so much effort that it is not worthwhile. The reason for the trouble is that the situation is a little more complicated than it looks. By custom, the + sign has been left out between the whole number and the fraction. The problem should really be written: $(3 + \frac{1}{2}) \times (5 + \frac{3}{4})$. It is actually two separate addition problems whose *answers* must be multiplied together. This is the reason that pencil and paper arithmetic always requires you to change a mixed number to an improper fraction before you do the multiplication, thus: $\frac{7}{2} \times \frac{23}{4}$.

Some sophisticated calculators have a separate memory. So in a problem like this, the value of one factor can be obtained, then "parked" in the memory while the main part of the calculator evaluates the other part.

However, there are some tricks that can help with this problem. Let's review what must be done to a mixed number before it can be used in a multiplication or division problem. It first must be changed to an improper fraction. This is done by multiplying the whole number by the denominator, then adding the numerator. Some examples:

$$3\frac{1}{2} = \frac{7}{2} \qquad 5\frac{1}{4} = \frac{21}{4}$$

$$7\frac{7}{8} = \frac{63}{8} \qquad 11\frac{15}{16} = \frac{191}{16}$$

The next step is to enter the number into the calculator by entering the numerator, then dividing by the denominator. However, if you have used the calculator to figure the improper fraction, then it is already in the calculator.

With that background, let's look at the various shortcuts. If both fractions are excessively complicated, figure the improper fraction for one of them on the calculator, and write the result. Next, figure the second one on the calculator and reenter the first one. For example, calculate.

$$118\frac{5}{17} \times 223\frac{1}{7}$$

Step 1: **17** $\boxed{\times}$ **118** $\boxed{+}$ **5** $\boxed{=}$ 2011

Make note: $\dfrac{2011}{17}$

Step 2: **7** $\boxed{\times}$ **223** $\boxed{+}$ **1** $\boxed{\div}$ **7**

This completes the entry of the second fraction. Now re-enter $\boxed{\times}$ and the first one:

2011 $\boxed{\div}$ **17** $\boxed{=}$ 26396.486

Problems are rarely this complicated. If one of the terms is very large, and the other one simple, enter the big one first, using the calculator to change it to an improper fraction. Then change the second term mentally, either to an improper fraction or directly to its decimal value.

Let's see how all these methods can be combined. We'll assume the person solving this problem is just fair with mental arithmetic. Here's the problem:

$$4 \tfrac{1}{2} \times 3 \tfrac{1}{6} \times 7 \tfrac{5}{8} \times 37 \tfrac{4}{19}$$

As he looks over the problem, these are his thoughts, "OK, the $4 \tfrac{1}{2}$ I can enter as 4.5. I'd better think of $3 \tfrac{1}{6}$ as a $\tfrac{19}{6}$. I don't really trust myself with the $7 \tfrac{5}{8}$, so I'll do that now and write down the result:

8 $\boxed{\times}$ **7** $\boxed{+}$ **5** $\boxed{=}$ 61

And I'll begin the problem with that nasty one on the end."

He now sees the problem as:

$$37 \boxed{\times} 19 \boxed{+} 4 \boxed{\div} 19 \boxed{=} 37.210526$$
$$\boxed{\times} 61 \boxed{\div} 8 \boxed{\times} 19 \boxed{\div} 6 \boxed{\times} 4.5 \boxed{=} 4043.1559$$

Check each of the calculator entries against the problem, and make sure you see where each figure and operation came from.

Division involving mixed numbers is handled in the same way, except of course, that the signs are switched as described in the division section.

Here are several problems for practice, with the answers given. There may be minor differences in the last decimal place depending on the method you like to use:

$$58 \tfrac{7}{13} \times 3 \tfrac{1}{2} \times 5 \tfrac{1}{4} \div 2 = \qquad 537.8221$$

$$8 \tfrac{11}{64} \times 5 \tfrac{7}{32} \times 8 \tfrac{3}{8} \times 4 \tfrac{1}{2} = \qquad 1607.2577$$

$$5.75 \times 3 \tfrac{1}{4} \times \tfrac{17}{4} = \qquad 79.421875$$

$$8 \tfrac{1}{2} \div 4 \tfrac{3}{4} \times 18 \tfrac{1}{4} \times 37 \tfrac{23}{49} = \qquad 1223.6712$$

$$14083 \tfrac{3}{4} \times 7 \tfrac{1}{8} \times 25 \tfrac{1}{2} = \qquad 2558841.1$$

Converting Decimal Fractions to Common Fractions

A procedure exists for the *exact* conversion of any repeating decimal fraction into a common fraction. For instance, it can be shown that .068181 . . . = $\tfrac{3}{44}$. It has little interest for us, because the practical reason for changing a decimal fraction to a common fraction is so that *you* can specify the denominator. If you're doing carpentry, you may want your numerical quantities in eighths of an inch. If you're doing work in a system requiring twelfths, such as inches-and-feet, or units-dozens-grosses, then you may want a denominator of 12. Therefore we will use a simpler method.

When you have your final result of a problem displayed on the calculator, it will generally include a decimal fraction. If you want to convert to a common fraction, make your written note of the whole-number portion of the result, and subtract it, leaving only the decimal fraction. Now multiply the display by the desired denominator, and the display will give you your numerator.

With procedures like this, some people have difficulty remembering whether to multiply or divide. Remember that when you put a common fraction *into* the calculator, you *divide*, because that's what the fraction bar means. Therefore, when you want to get a common fraction *out* of the calculator, you must do the reverse and *multiply* by the denominator.

Let's say that you have done a calculation concerned with some carpentry work, and wanted the result in eighths of an inch. The display says that your measurement is 39.8125 inches. First, write the 39 inches for your record, subtract it from the display, and then multiply by the desired denominator of 8:

$$39.8125 \;\boxed{-}\; 39 \;\boxed{\times}\; 8 \;\boxed{=}\; 6.5$$

Therefore that decimal fraction represented $\frac{6.5}{8}$ which you must either round down to $\frac{6}{8}$ or up to $\frac{7}{8}$ depending on your purpose.

Here are some sample problems, with answers given in the right column. For practice, enter the entire number, then subtract:

State 17.682 to the nearest 4th $\qquad$ $17\frac{3}{4}$

State 85.317 to the nearest 16th $\qquad$ $85\frac{5}{16}$

State 1857.63 to the nearest 12th $\qquad$ $1857\frac{8}{12}$

State 11.3 to the nearest 32nd $\qquad$ $11\frac{10}{32}$

State 3.14 to the nearest 7th $\qquad$ $3\frac{1}{7}$

SUMMARY

You now have at your disposal a facility for dealing with fractions with a speed, accuracy, and ease that a few years ago would have bordered on the miraculous. But unless you have an extraordinary mind and memory, it is unlikely you have mastered these techniques in one reading. If you don't need these procedures at present, you know where to find them when you do.

If you do need them now, you will probably want to reread this section several times at intervals of a day or two. Rework the practice problems each time until they finally become natural and automatic.

CHAPTER 6
PERCENTAGE

A key part of human intelligence is the ability to form ideas or *concepts* that are general, not connected with any real or actual thing. We can think of the general idea "chair" without thinking of any particular chair. In the same way, we can think of a number or quantity without thinking of that quantity of some specific thing.

Arithmetic is the study of numbers, and an important part of that study is devoted to the numbers lying between 0 and 1, known as fractions. Fractions are usually expressed in decimal form, such as .25, or in common fraction, $\frac{1}{4}$. But there is a third way of expressing fractions that is quite practical. *Percentage* is almost always used to talk about the parts of some actual thing.

The Latin word *cent* means *hundred*, so *percent* means *per hundred*. When we say that 90% of a group of people have blue eyes, we mean: *If* there were a 100 of these people *then* 90 of them would have blue eyes.

Percent suggests that whenever we want to know something about the parts of things, or the distribution of things, we take a standard sample of 100 and count the things in that sample. The sample is always assumed to be the same size. So we are able, in our minds, to make vivid and understandable comparisons. If we say that a bank pays 5% interest, we mean that they pay $5 for each $100 on deposit;

this is just as true for the man with $17 in the bank, as it is
for the man with $1883.27.

So we come a full circle in understanding the way we
think. Even though the use of percentage is confined to the
real working world, its usefulness still depends on our ability
to imagine, to visualize, to say, "*If* there were exactly 100 of
these, *then* . . . ."

There were some good reasons for choosing this sample
size of 100. It is a nice number, big enough to allow fractions
to be expressed with considerable accuracy, yet small enough
to be understandable. Most important, however, is that it fits
exactly into our decimal number system.

Converting a decimal fraction to percent only requires
moving the decimal point two places to the right. Therefore,
.25 converts to 25%; .03 converts to 3%; and 1.22 converts to
122%. Obviously, converting a percent statement to decimal
fraction form is the reverse procedure: The decimal point is
moved two places to the left, so that 17% is converted to .17.

Converting a common fraction to a percentage is a
two-step job. First, the division indicated by the fraction bar
should be done, then the decimal point moved two places to
the right.

$$\tfrac{3}{4} = 3 \div 4 = .75 \text{ or } 75\%$$

On the calculator, it is possible to move the decimal point
without disturbing any of the digits. To move it two spaces
to the right, multiply by 100. To move it two spaces to the
left, divide by 100. The calculator procedure for translating $\tfrac{3}{4}$ into 75% is:

$$3 \boxed{\div} 4 \boxed{=} .75 \boxed{\times} 100 \boxed{=} 75.$$

It is entirely proper to use terms such as 15.75% or 15 $\frac{3}{4}$% if a high degree of accuracy is really required. This should not be done unless it is essential. The great virtue of percentage is its clarity and simplicity. Cluttering it with unneeded detail dilutes this value. Exceptions to this general policy occur when you want to indicate an exact fraction in percentage terms, most frequently 33 $\frac{1}{3}$% for $\frac{1}{3}$, and 66 $\frac{2}{3}$% for $\frac{2}{3}$.

One of the most valuable thinking techniques in mathematics is to invent a simple version of the problem that puzzles you. You can then solve the simple problem in your head, and use that solution as a model for solving the complex problem.

We are going to suggest that you adopt this statement as your model for thinking about percentage:

$$10 \text{ is } 25\% \text{ of } 40$$

First, let's change the words in it to their mathematical equivalents:

$$10 = .25 \times 40$$

Notice particularly the translation of the word *of* into the symbol for *multiply*. If you will remember that *of* means *times,* much of the difficulty with percentage will disappear.

There are three numbers in our basic statement. Any one of them could be missing, thus creating the three basic kinds of percentage problems.

The first kind of problem is in the form: What is 25% of 40, or ? = .25 × 40. The solution to this problem is obviously to perform the multiplication:

$$.25 \boxed{\times} \ 40 \boxed{=} \ 10$$

This form of the problem is the only one that uses multiplication, because it is the only one where the numbers on both sides of the *times* sign are known.

The next form of the problem is: 10 is what percent of 40. In symbols: 10 = .?? × 40. We can't multiply because the number on one side of the *times* sign is missing. If we can't multiply, then we must divide, but do we divide 10 by 40, or do we divide 40 by 10? There are three ways to think about this. Look at all three, and pick the one that makes the most sense to you:

1) I am trying to find a percent, which is the same as a fraction, so I must put the small number over the big one:

$$\tfrac{10}{40} = 10 \div 40 = .25 = 25\%.$$

2) I am trying to find a percent, which is less than one. If I divided 40 by 10, I'd get a whole number, so it must be 10 divided by 40.

3) I already know the answer is 25%, which is the same as $\tfrac{10}{40}$, so I must divide 10 by 40.

Remember, we are not really trying to solve this problem; we're setting up a mental model for solving problems such as: 87 is 19% of what number?

The third basic form of a percentage problem is: 10 is 25% of what number, or 10 = ? × .25? Again, we cannot multiply because the number on one side of the "times" sign is missing, so we must divide. And again comes the question: Do I divide .25 by 10, or do I divide 10 by .25?

And again there are three ways of thinking about it:

1) If I divided .25 by 10, I'd be getting part of a "percent," but I don't want part of a "percent," I want a "number." So I have to divide 10 by 25.
2) I'm looking for a "big" number. If I divided .25 by 10 I'd get a very small number, but if I divided 10 by .25, I'd get a number much larger than 10.
3) I already know the answer is 40, and the only way to get it is to divide 10 by .25.

Let's summarize these three basic problems and their solutions:

What is 25% of 40   Answer: .25 × 40 = 10
10 is what percent of 40   Answer: 10 ÷ 40 = .25, or 25%
10 is 25% of what number   Answer: 10 ÷ .25 = 40

This discussion has strongly implied that a percentage is always a *proper* fraction of a number, that is, a fraction representing only a part of a unit. While this is usually true, it is not always true. For instance, someone who used to earn $200 a week and now earns $250 a week, could say, "My present salary is 125% of my old salary." He is saying that he now earns $125 in the time it used to take him to earn $100. This idea of a percentage of more than 100 is very useful in some problems. Let's say you wondered about the *total* cost to you of a stereo record player tagged at $139.95, but subject to a 7% sales tax. You could figure the tax:

$$139.95 \boxed{\times} .07 \boxed{=} \ 9.7965 \text{ or } \$9.80$$

You then have to add the list price and the tax:

$$139.95 \boxed{+} 9.80 \boxed{=} \ 149.75$$

But look at it this way. You are going to pay 100% of the cost plus 7% of the cost, for a total of 107%. Why not multiply the price by 107% and save a step:

$$139.95 \boxed{\times} 1.07 \boxed{=} 149.7465 \text{ or } \$149.75$$

This provides the key to a problem which is often confusing. You tell a friend your stereo cost you $149.75 *with* tax, and he wonders what the tagged price was. He can reverse your procedure and calculate:

$$149.75 \boxed{\div} 1.07 \boxed{=} 139.95327 \text{ or } \$139.95$$

With this background, you should now read the more advanced discussion of Percentage in Chapter 10 and Appendix I of this book, and do the practice problems shown there.

CHAPTER 7
EXPONENTS, POWERS, AND ROOTS

When we want to show that a certain number is to be multiplied by itself, once or several times, an *exponent* provides a convenient shorthand way of indicating this. For instance, $6 \times 6 \times 6$ can be written 6^3, or 5×5 can be written 5^2.

The number being multiplied by itself is called the *base*. The small raised number which tells the number of times the base is to be used is called an *exponent*. The number which results from this multiplication process is called a *power* of the base.

The formal way to say 7^4 is "seven raised to the fourth power," however, this phrase is almost always shortened to, "seven to the 4th." Please, *please* do not ever say, "seven-four," even in your own private thinking.

Although it is entirely correct to read 5^2 as "five to the second," and to read 4^3 as, "four to the third," most mathematicians use a different phrase for these two powers. These diagrams indicate why:

5^2 is said "five squared" 4^3 is said, "four cubed"

$5 \times 5 = 5^2 = 25$ $4 \times 4 \times 4 = 4^3 = 64$

For the first few times these symbols are used, we'll give you a reminder of the proper way to say them.

A great variety of different ideas and methods has grown from this simple shortcut. The technique of raising numbers to various powers is so widely used that your calculator has been provided with a convenient way to perform this operation.

We could find the value of 5^2 (five squared) by entering 5 ⨯ 5 = 25. However, there is a shortcut. Try entering 5 ⨯ = . Any number showing on the display will be squared when the ⨯ and = keys are operated. Try squaring the numbers 2 through 9 using this procedure.

To raise numbers to the 3rd and higher powers, you must move the CHAIN-CONSTANT switch to the CONSTANT position. To find the value of 8^3 (eight cubed) enter:

CONSTANT 8 ⨯ = = 512.

Notice that the = key is pressed one less time than the power desired.

When numbers are raised to successively higher powers, they grow very rapidly. The term 5^{10} looks small and simple because it is so easy to write, but it is a huge number. With the switch in CONSTANT position, enter 5 ⨯ = , then continue to press the = key and watch how quickly the powers of 5 grow to tremendous size. The first time you press the = key, you get five to the second power. Count as you continue to operate it, saying, "third, fourth, fifth . . ." and so on.

We can do arithmetic with the exponent itself, obtaining some very interesting results. Check the truthfulness of these statements on your calculator:

$$6^2 = 6 \times 6 = 36$$
$$6^3 = 6 \times 6 \times 6 = 216$$
$$6^5 = 6 \times 6 \times 6 \times 6 \times 6 = 7776$$

$$\left.\right\} 36 \times 216 = 7776$$

Notice that when we multiply the result of 6^2 by the result of 6^3, we obtain the result of 6^5. Now look at the exponents in this operation, namely 2, 3, and 5. We know that 5 is the *sum* of 2 and 3, but this was a multiplication problem! Yet this does make sense. Shouldn't these two results be the same? That is, we may have:

$$(6 \times 6) \times (6 \times 6 \times 6) = 7776$$

or

$$6 \times 6 \times 6 \times 6 \times 6 = 7776 !$$

In a limited way, we seem to have reduced the complicated problem of multiplication to the much simpler process of addition.

Will this process work in reverse? Can the powers of numbers be divided by subtracting their exponents? Here is 8 raised to three different powers. You should double-check all this on your calculator:

$$8^2 = 8 \times 8 = 64$$

$$8^4 = 8 \times 8 \times 8 \times 8 = 4096$$

$$8^6 = 8 \times 8 \times 8 \times 8 \times 8 \times 8 = 262,144$$

8^6 divided by 8^2 should be $8^{(6-2)}$, or 8^4

$$262,144 \div 64 = 4096$$

As we would expect, this process works just as well in division as it did in multiplication.

It is very clear that 5^2 means 5×5, and that 5^3 means $5 \times 5 \times 5$. But we could write other kinds of numbers in the exponent position, such as 0, or negative numbers, or fractions. What would they mean?

Let's start with 2^1. It seems likely that it means just plain 2, but let's verify it. We know that subtracting exponents results in division, and we know that 2^2 is 4, and that 2^3 is 8. If we divide 8 by 4, we obtain 2. This is the same as saying that if we divide 2^3 by 2^2, we obtain 2. But:

$$\frac{2^3}{2^2} = 2^{(3 - 2)} \text{ or } 2^1$$

Thus, we have shown that a number to the 1st power is the number itself. Raising it to the first power does not change it.

Next, let's examine 3^0. For many people this is confusing and difficult to understand. On the other hand, 3^2 is easy; it means take two 3s and multiply them together. Even 3^1 is not too difficult to grasp. It means take one 3, and since there is nothing you can do with it, leave it alone. But 3^0 seems to say, "Don t take any 3s and do something with them." This is obvious foolishness, yet 3^0 will fit into the system. Again, remember that division is accomplished by subtracting exponents. Now find the value of this fraction by the subtraction of exponents:

$$\frac{3^2}{3^2}$$

Therefore, 3^2 divided by 3^2 would be $3^{(2-2)}$, or 3^0. Yet we know that 3^2 divided by 3^2 means 9 divided by 9. We know also that any number divided by itself gives a result of 1. Thus, we have shown that 3^0 equals 1. If this same reasoning were applied to another number, the result would be the same. Therefore: Any number raised to the 0 power is equal to 1. The single exception is 0^0, which has no meaning. Now don't fight this, and don't try to put it into words. The fact that a number raised to the 0 power equals 1 follows as a logical necessity from the rest of the exponent system, so it is accepted as being true "by definition."

However, the same kind of reasoning that proved that n^0 equals 1 can be further applied, with other interesting and worthwhile results. Let's examine the meaning of:

$$\frac{4^2}{4^3}$$

When we expand and perform this we have:

$$\frac{4^2}{4^3} = \frac{16}{64} = \frac{1}{4}$$

But if we perform the division by subtracting exponents, we obtain:

$$4^2 \div 4^3 = 4^{(2-3)} = 4^{-1}$$

We now have a negative exponent, and have shown that $4^{-1} = \frac{1}{4}$.

Let's do that one more time, this time using:

$$\frac{2^2}{2^5} = \frac{4}{32} = \frac{1}{8}$$

We can also express:

$$\frac{1}{8} \text{ as } \frac{1}{2^3}$$

But if we perform the division by subtracting exponents, we obtain:

$$\frac{2^2}{2^5} = 2^2 \div 2^5 = 2^{(2-5)} = 2^{-3}$$

We have now demonstrated that:

$$2^{-3} = \frac{1}{2^3}$$

We previously showed that: $4^{-1} = \frac{1}{4}$. In sorting this in our minds, the first thing we can say is that a negative exponent means a fraction. The denominator of that fraction is the number raised to the corresponding positive power.

The name of a number which has been inverted is the *reciprocal* of the original number. Thus $\frac{1}{5}$ is the reciprocal of 5. A number with a negative exponent is the reciprocal of the same number with the same positive exponent:

the reciprocal of 9 is $\frac{1}{9}$

the reciprocal of 3^2 is $\frac{1}{3^2}$

the reciprocal of 3^2 is 3^{-2}, because $3^{-2} = \frac{1}{3^2}$

The calculator is capable of directly computing the value of numbers with negative exponents, just as it can compute the value of positive exponents. You will recall that to raise a number to a power, the CHAIN-CONSTANT switch was put in the CONSTANT position, the number entered, followed by $\boxed{\times}$, then the $\boxed{=}$ key pressed one *less* time than the power:

$$2^5 = 2 \boxed{\times} \quad \overset{\text{``2''}}{\boxed{=}} \quad \overset{\text{``3''}}{\boxed{=}} \quad \overset{\text{``4''}}{\boxed{=}} \quad \overset{\text{``5''}}{\boxed{=}} \quad 32$$

In a similar fashion, the value of 2^{-5} can be found, using the $\boxed{\div}$ key instead of the $\boxed{\times}$ key. The major difference is that the $\boxed{=}$ key must be operated one *more* time than the power desired. Here's why:

$$2^{-5} = 2 \boxed{\div} \qquad \text{(this is } 2^1\text{)}$$
$$\boxed{=} \qquad \text{(this is } 2^0 \text{ power; note the 1 in display)}$$
$$\boxed{=} \qquad \text{(this is } 2^{-1} \text{which equals } \tfrac{1}{2} \text{ or .5)}$$
$$\boxed{=} \qquad \text{(this is } 2^{-2}\text{)}$$
$$\boxed{=} \qquad (2^{-3})$$
$$\boxed{=} \qquad (2^{-4})$$
$$\boxed{=} \qquad (2^{-5})$$

You should have a result of .03125. Find its reciprocal by pressing $\boxed{\div}$ $\boxed{=}$ $\boxed{=}$. The result of 32 is 2^5, which is the reciprocal of 2^{-5}.

We have now seen exponents using positive numbers, zero, and negative numbers, but what of fractions? Could we have exponents like $5^{\frac{1}{2}}$ or $3^{.25}$ and what would they mean? We can attack this question in the same way we did the others, but first we had better examine the general questions of roots.

We have seen how we can raise a number to a power by multiplying it by itself. That is, 4^3 means $4 \times 4 \times 4$. It should be possible to undo this operation. Just as division will undo multiplication, so there should also be a process which will undo raising to a power.

This process is called "finding the root" or "extracting the root." The system used for naming exponents is also used for naming roots. Here are some examples:

4 squared is 16. The square root of 16 is 4.

3 to the fifth power is 243. The fifth root of 243 is 3.

The symbol used to indicate this operation is this sign: $\sqrt{}$ which is called a radical. (This term comes from the Latin *radix*, meaning *root*. A political radical is someone who wants to tear everything down to the roots and start over again.) Thus, the symbol $\sqrt{16}$ is read, "the square root of 16" and has a value of 4, because $4 \times 4 = 16$.

If a root other than a square root is indicated, a small number is placed over the radical sign to show this. For example, $\sqrt[3]{64}$ is read, "the cube root of 64." It has a value of 4, because $4 \times 4 \times 4 = 4^3 = 64$. Similarly the expression, $\sqrt[8]{22}$ would be read, "the 8th root of 22."

It is much easier to talk about the root of a number than it is to find its value. Considering the question of square roots, there are relatively few numbers which are perfect squares (for instance 4, 9, 16, 25, 36, and so forth) and only perfect squares have square roots which are integers, or whole numbers. All other square roots are numbers which are called *irrational numbers*. An irrational number is a number which will never "come out even." If the computation is continued, its decimal is endless, and the decimal can never be converted into an exact fraction. Thus, most roots are approximations in the form they are actually used. Of course they can always be computed to whatever level of accuracy is needed.

Finding the value of a root of a number presents an interesting problem. In most arithmetic problems, you start with two numbers, and combine them as $6 + 2$, or 5×8. But when you have the question: What is the square root of 76," where do you start? What do you begin to do first? The lazy and practical answer is that you look it up in a table of square roots that has been prepared by someone else.

There are several procedures for finding a square root or higher roots and they depend, in principle, on making an estimate and then gradually refining that estimate. You will find one such procedure, especially adapted to the calculator, explained in detail earlier in this book.

We observed that two numbers could be multiplied by adding their exponents. It is a small additional step to understand that a number can be raised to a power by *multiplying* its exponent. To square a number, we multiply its exponent by 2. For instance, 8 has the same meaning as

2^3. Therefore 8^2 should have the same meaning as $2^{(3 \times 2)}$, or 2^6. Check 8^2 and 2^6 on your calculator to determine if they have the same value.

To raise a number to the third power (that is, to cube it), we multiply its exponent by 3; and to raise a number to the 10th power, we multiply its exponent by 10.

There is one demonstration of the truth of this statement that is so simple, yet it makes good sense. We know that any number can be expressed as that number with an exponent of 1. In other words, 9^1 means 9. It follows, then, that 9^3 must equal $9^{(1 \times 3)}$.

We saw that finding the root of a number was undoing the process of raising it to a power, just as division undoes multiplication. If we can raise a number to a power by multiplying its exponent, we should be able to find its root by dividing its exponent. For example: $\sqrt{729} = 27$. But also $729 = 3^6$. Therefore $3^{(6 \div 2)}$, or 3^3 should also equal 27. And it does. You might recheck these figures on your calculator.

We are now finally at the point where we can answer the question that was raised some time ago. What is the meaning of a fractional exponent? What does $16^{\frac{1}{2}}$ mean, for instance? The answer should be quite clear by now. That is:

$$16^{\frac{1}{2}}$$

can be obtained by dividing the exponent of 16^1 by 2. That is, $16^{(1 \div 2)}$ is $16^{\frac{1}{2}}$. When we divide the exponent of a number by 2, we are obtaining the number's square root. Therefore:

$$16^{\frac{1}{2}}$$

should be the square root of 16.

Let's check that with another example. We know that 9^2 is 81; therefore $\sqrt{81} = 9$. But is it also true that:

$$81^{\frac{1}{2}} = 9$$

If it is, it should also be true that $9^2 = 81$ and that:

$$81^{(\frac{1}{2} \times 2)} = 81 \text{ Thus } \frac{1}{2} \times 2 = 1.$$

Point proven.

So we have two ways to indicate the root of a number; the radical sign, as in $\sqrt{16}$, and the fractional exponent, as in: $16^{\frac{1}{2}}$.

Finding the value of fractional powers and roots is most easily accomplished using logarithms, and in Appendix I to this book you will find a table of logarithms, and an explanation of their use for this purpose.

LEARNING MORE

If you are interested in further study and practice in arithmetic, the easiest and least expensive way to buy a textbook is to purchase a paperback review of 8th year mathematics in any store carrying school supplies. A library will have a wide assortment of interesting books. Some of the

best writing on popular mathematics has been done by
Martin Gardner, who has conducted a column called "Mathe-
matical Games" in the *Scientific American* for many years.
Most of these columns have been republished in book form.

Many other authors have written excellent books which
present the ideas of mathematics in an interesting way, with
varying degrees of numerical detail, so that something can be
found to meet every taste. One of these books is a two-
volume set by J. Wimbish, *Mathematics, A Humanestic
Approach* and *Readings for Mathematics, A Humanestic
Approach*, Wadsworth Publishing Company, Belmont,
California, 1972.

APPLICATIONS

CHAPTER 8
AREAS OF PLANE FIGURES

Many area problems were solved thousands of years ago by the ancient Egyptians. They needed these results as they attempted to restore the boundaries of farms in the fertile Nile valley after the annual flooding obliterated the markers. Remember that to find the area of enclosed shapes means to find how many square inches, or square miles or square "whatevers" there are contained in that figure. The rules for solving these problems move in a logical progression, and once they are seen arranged in order they are relatively easy to remember.

THE RECTANGLE

A rectangle is one of the most familiar man-made shapes. Its opposite sides are parallel and of equal length, and all of its angles are right angles.

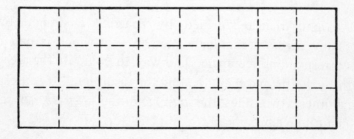

Finding the area of a rectangle is a matter of counting the unit squares it contains for a given unit of measure. The easy way to do this is to count the number of units along the length and along the width, then multiply these two numbers. The figure shown has 3 rows, each containing 8 squares. Thus, the area is 3 × 8 = 24. The general rule for the area of a rectangle is:

Length $\boxed{\times}$ **Width** $\boxed{=}$ Area

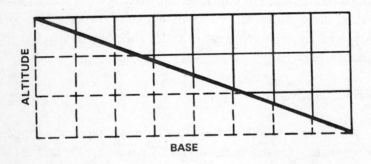

ALTITUDE

BASE

THE RIGHT TRIANGLE

A right triangle, formed by drawing a straight line diagonally across a rectangle, has an area which is half of the corresponding rectangle. The way to compute the area is length by width, and then dividing the result by 2. It is useful to call these two sides the *base* and the *altitude*, so the formula for area becomes:

Base $\boxed{\times}$ **Altitude** $\boxed{\div}$ 2 $\boxed{=}$ Area

In the triangle shown above, the base is 8, the altitude is 3, and the area is:

$$8 \boxed{\times} 3 \boxed{\div} 2 \boxed{=} 12 \text{ (square units)}$$

It is important that this formula be applied to the two sides which *meet at the right angle*. If the third side (the hypotenuse), which in a right triangle will be the **longest** side, is used, the result will be in error.

Here are several practice problems. The triangles have been turned in different ways so you must identify the two sides adjoining the right angle. Check your answers against those given:

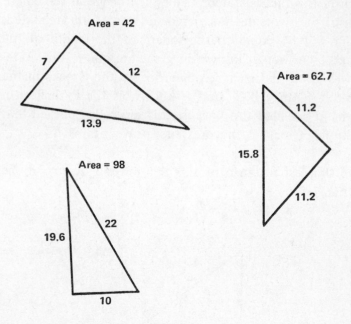

The Sum of the Squares of the Sides

Men who have constructed buildings, from the palaces of ancient Babylon 3500 years ago to the newest suburban home, have used a fundamental fact of geometry to make their buildings come out square.

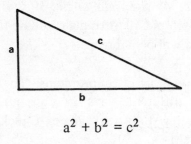

$$a^2 + b^2 = c^2$$

In English, this fact is stated: In a right triangle, if the length of each of the two sides is squared and the results are added, this sum will be equal to the square of the length of the hypotenuse. Although known in great antiquity, this statement was given its first rigorous proof by the Greeks in the 5th or 6th century B.C., and is known as the Pythagorean Theorem. It is called this because it is generally believed that a well known Greek, Pythagoras, first proved it.

The simplest instance of this relationship occurs in the 3-4-5 triangle.

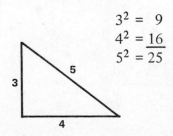

$$3^2 = 9$$
$$4^2 = \underline{16}$$
$$5^2 = 25$$

The Pythagoreans were a religious cult, who based their beliefs on the mathematical nature of the world. It is easy to see how they could attach mystical significance to this beautifully simple relationship. Although all right triangles obey this law, only certain of them "come out even" so that all three sides are whole numbers or simple fractions. If two of the sides are whole numbers, usually the third side can only be approximated. Of course it can be approximated to any desired degree of accuracy, for instance:

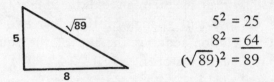

$$5^2 = 25$$
$$8^2 = 64$$
$$(\sqrt{89})^2 = 89$$

The hypotenuse is the square root of 89, which is approximately 9.433981132 . . . .

The simplest and most widely used application of this rule is in construction when one needs to set up a right angle. For instance, let's suppose a carpenter wants to place two 2 × 4s at precise right angles. He can place a mark on one of them exactly three feet from the corner, and on the other, four feet from the corner. He can then place his rule diagonally and adjust them until there is exactly five feet between the marks. And, of course, if he wants greater accuracy, he can double or triple the triangle to 6-8-10, or 9-12-15 without destroying the Pythagorean relationship.

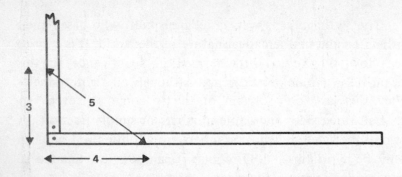

The Pythagorean Theorem gives us the ability to find the third side of any *right* triangle if the other two sides are known. The solution requires the use of the square root procedure for the calculator (page 48).

The basic statement, and the three procedures derived from it are given below:

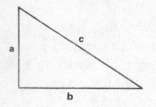

$$a^2 + b^2 = c^2$$
$$c = \sqrt{a^2 + b^2}$$
$$a = \sqrt{c^2 - b^2}$$
$$b = \sqrt{c^2 - a^2}$$

For example, find side b of this triangle:

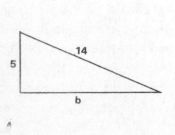

$$b = \sqrt{c^2 - a^2}$$
$$b = \sqrt{14^2 - 5^2}$$
$$b = \sqrt{196 - 25}$$
$$b = \sqrt{171}$$
$$b = 13.077, \text{ approx.}$$

Here are some Pythagorean triples, that is, whole numbers which exhibit the $a^2 + b^2 = c^2$ relationship. If you want to check them, remember that a number can be squared on the calculator by entering it, then pressing $\boxed{x}\ \boxed{=}$

5-12-13	9-40-41	20-21-29
7-24-25	11-60-61	28-45-53
8-15-17	12-35-37	48-55-73

THE PARALLELOGRAM

If a rectangle were made of four strips of wood nailed at each corner with a single nail, it would be possible to flatten it somewhat by letting the corners pivot, resulting in the shape below.

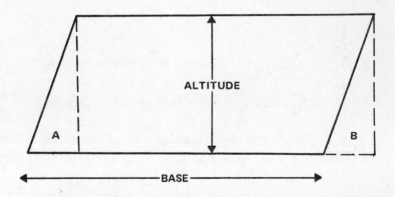

A parallelogram is a shape having opposite sides which are equal and parallel, but which do not meet at right angles. If the flattening process continued, the area of the parallelogram would grow smaller and finally disappear. Therefore the area of a parallelogram is always smaller than a rectangle with the same length sides.

The drawings below show a rectangle (1) which has been partially flattened into a parallelogram (2). If we draw the dotted lines at *right angles* to the top and bottom as shown, we make two triangles, A and B. We could cut off triangle A and move it over to B without changing either the area or the length of the base. We now have a new, smaller rectangle (3), and we can compute its area by the "length times width" formula.

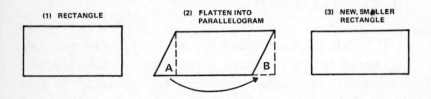

Thus, the formula for the area of a parallelogram is:

Base $\boxed{\times}$ **Altitude** $\boxed{=}$ **Area**

The altitude is *not* the length of one of the sides, but is measured along a new line drawn at right angles to the base.

Here are two practice problems. Check your results against those given:

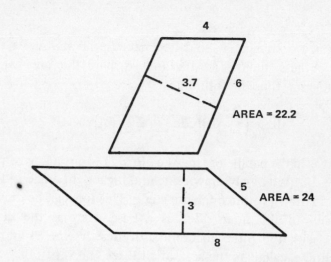

THE ACUTE TRIANGLE

A right triangle was formed by cutting a rectangle in half. Two other triangles can be formed by cutting a parallelogram in a similar way. Here is the first one, formed by cutting the parallelogram across the closer of the two pairs of corners:

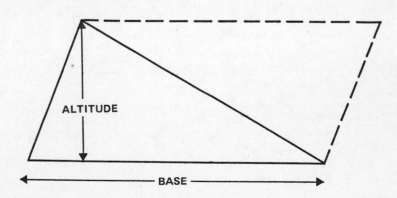

An acute triangle is so-called because all its angles are acute, or less than 90°. Its area is half the area of a parallelogram, thus the formula is:

Base $\boxed{\text{x}}$ Altitude $\boxed{\div}$ 2 $\boxed{=}$ Area

Just as in the parallelogram, the *altitude* is not a line of the triangle, but is a newly drawn line making a right angle to the base, and drawn to the opposite angle. This line can be drawn using any of the three sides as a base. Here is the same triangle with the three different altitudes drawn. Using the value shown, calculate the area of all three and verify that the results are the same within the limits of accuracy of the measurements.

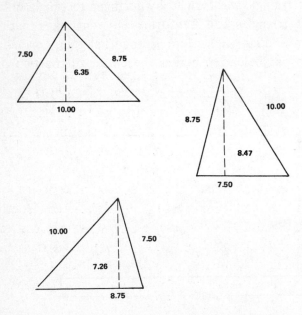

THE OBTUSE TRIANGLE

The other way to cut the parallelogram in half diagonally is across the more distant pair of corners:

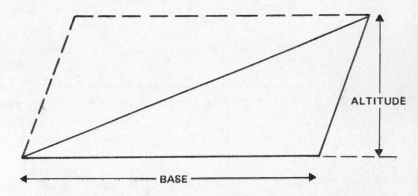

An obtuse triangle has one angle which is greater than 90°. However, the formula for the area remains the same:

$$\text{Base} \;\boxed{\times}\; \text{Altitude} \;\boxed{\div}\; 2 \;\boxed{=}\; \text{Area}$$

Any of the three sides may be used as the base in applying this formula, but observe that the altitude line lies outside the triangle in two of the three cases. These altitudes are drawn by extending the base far enough so that a right-angled line can be drawn to the opposite angle.

To readers who are not familiar with Euclidean geometry and with trigonometry, and who may ask how the length of the altitude is found, the answer is that we are confining ourselves here to practical geometry, in which the right angle is formed using a T-square or other right-angled shape, and the length of the altitude is measured with a ruler or tape.

Here is the same obtuse triangle drawn with the three different altitudes. Calculate the three areas, and verify that they are the same.

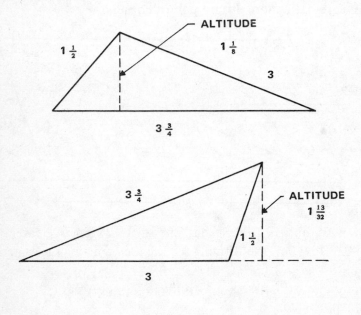

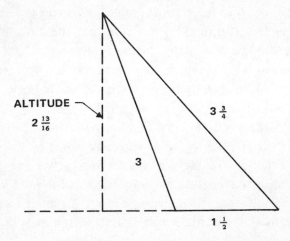

OTHER FOUR-SIDED FIGURES

The Trapezoid

A trapezoid is a four-sided figure in which only two sides are parallel, but are of different lengths. As a result, the ends are not parallel, and do not even have to be the same length.

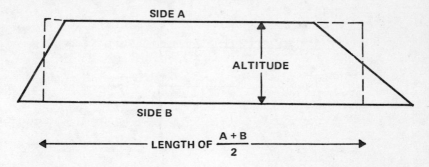

Notice that a trapezoid could be made into a rectangle by flipping the small triangle at each end upwards and rotating it. The pivot point is the middle of the end line, and the distance between these pivot points is the length of the newly formed rectangle.

Also notice that these pivot points are halfway between the top and bottom lines, and that the distance between them could be found by averaging the length of the top and bottom lines, that is, by adding them together and then dividing by 2. Thus, the area of a trapezoid is:

Side A $\boxed{+}$ Side B $\boxed{\div}$ 2 $\boxed{\times}$ Altitude $\boxed{=}$ Area

The altitude is a newly drawn line at right angles to the two parallel sides.

Here are two trapezoids. Calculate their area and check
your answer with the answer given.

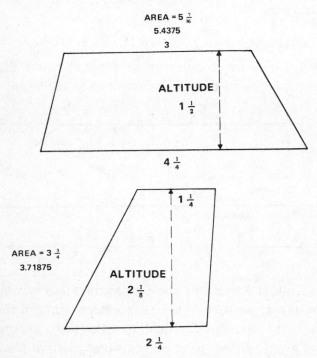

AREA = 5 $\frac{7}{16}$

5.4375

3

ALTITUDE

1 $\frac{1}{2}$

4 $\frac{1}{4}$

1 $\frac{1}{4}$

AREA = 3 $\frac{3}{4}$

3.71875

ALTITUDE

2 $\frac{1}{8}$

2 $\frac{1}{4}$

The Quadrilateral

There is no elementary formula for finding the area of a
four-sided figure in which none of the sides are parallel.

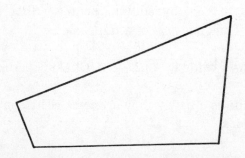

A quadrilateral's area is most easily measured by dividing it into simpler shapes, calculating these areas separately, and then adding them. Such a shape can always be broken down into right triangles and a trapezoid by drawing new altitude lines.

If the figure contains a side with acute angles at both ends, erect both altitude lines on the side, going to the two opposite angles.

If it contains only one acute angle, or if the two acute angles are diagonally opposite, then start by drawing an altitude from a side to an obtuse angle. Then draw the second altitude using the *first altitude* as a base.

Sometimes a bit of juggling is required, but a combination can always be found. Observe that the trapezoid that results always has one rectangular end, and that this end, therefore, is also the altitude of the trapezoid. These two practice examples should make these points clear. Compute the areas and check whether your answers agree with the answers given.

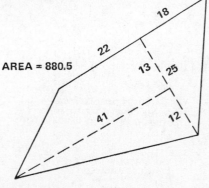

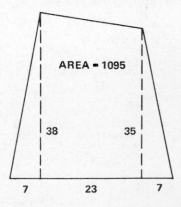

There is a rather complex formula for the area of a general quadrilateral which you might enjoy using, if you like this sort of thing for fun or for practice using the calculator. An example is given, together with the correct answer.

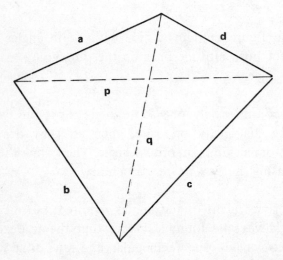

$$\text{Area} = \tfrac{1}{4}\sqrt{4p^2q^2 - (b^2 + d^2 - a^2 - c^2)^2}$$

For example, if $a = 5$, $b = 6$, $c = 7$, $d = 4$, $p = 8$, and $q = 7.1$, then the area is 27.9.

THE CIRCLE

The names of the parts of a circle are:

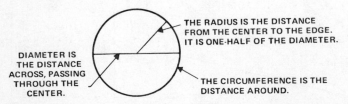

THE RADIUS IS THE DISTANCE FROM THE CENTER TO THE EDGE. IT IS ONE-HALF OF THE DIAMETER.

DIAMETER IS THE DISTANCE ACROSS, PASSING THROUGH THE CENTER.

THE CIRCUMFERENCE IS THE DISTANCE AROUND.

If the diameter were picked up and curved around the circumference, about $3\frac{1}{7}$ lengths would be needed. This value, which is true for all circles, is named by the Greek letter π (pi).

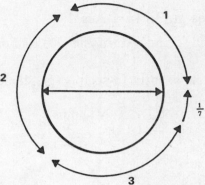

The decimal value of π is approximately 3.14. For extremely accurate work, the value 3.14159 may be used. The short form will cause an error of less than one inch when figuring the circumference of a 50-foot diameter circle, and therefore is more than adequate for all ordinary work.

If the diameter is known, the circumference is:

Diameter $\boxed{\times}$ 3.14 $\boxed{=}$ Circumference

If the circumference is known, the diameter is:

Circumference $\boxed{\div}$ 3.14 $\boxed{=}$ Diameter

The radius is one-half the diameter. The formula for the area of a circle is $\pi \times r^2$. Set up for the calculator it is:

Radius $\boxed{\times}$ $\boxed{=}$ $\boxed{\times}$ 3.14 $\boxed{=}$ Area

To find the radius when the area is known is a two-step problem requiring the extraction of a square root.

Step 1. **Area** $\div$ **3.14** $=$ Ans. 1

Step 2. Find square root of Ans. 1 = Radius

When a circle is cut into sectors (pie-shaped pieces), the names of the parts are:

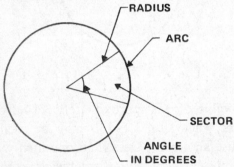

When the radius and the angle are known, the length of the arc can be found:

3.14 $\times$ **Radius** $\times$ **Angle** $\div$ **180** $=$ Length of arc

When the radius and angle are known, the area of the sector can be found:

Radius $\times$ $=$ $\times$ **3.14** $\times$ **Angle** $\div$ **360** $=$ Area of sector

This small body of rules will solve most problems involving the circle. Here are a few practice problems. The answers are given so you can check your results:

Answers are
rounded

7.21
Find circumference . . . 45.2788
45.3

196
Find area 120,626.24

11
Find area of sector . . . 52.769444
50° 52.8

19
Find length of arc . . . 13.257777
40°

Area of sector: 14 . . 56
Find area of circle
90°

THE ELLIPSE

When a circle is viewed at an angle or is seen in a perspective drawing, it appears to be "flattened." The same shape is generated when a cylinder is cut at an angle, as is often done by butchers slicing salami or bologna.

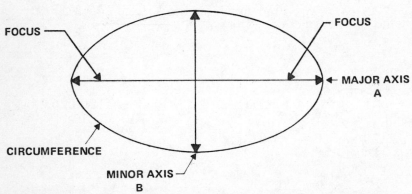

An ellipse is an appealing shape. It is often used in designs or in garden layouts. Although popularly called an oval, this is not quite correct. *Oval* comes from the root meaning *egg*, and properly refers to a shape similar to the ellipse, but smaller at one end.

The area of an ellipse can be calculated:

3.14 $\boxed{\times}$ Major Axis $\boxed{\times}$ Minor Axis $\boxed{\div}$ 4 $\boxed{=}$ Area

The circumference of an ellipse cannot be determined exactly, but this approximation is adequate for most purposes:

$$\pi \times \sqrt{\frac{A^2 + B^2}{2}} = \text{Circumference}$$

Set up for the calculator, this becomes:

Step 1. **Major axis** $\boxed{x}$ $\boxed{=}$ Ans. 1

Step 2. **Minor axis** $\boxed{x}$ $\boxed{=}$ Ans. 2

Step 3. $\sqrt{\text{Ans. 1} + \text{Ans. 2}}$ = Ans. 3
See square root procedure.

Step 4. Ans. 3 $\boxed{x}$ 3.14 $\boxed{=}$ Approximate Circumference

There is a draftsman's instrument for drawing ellipses, however, the method given below is accurate enough for most purposes if carried out with care. Although described in terms of a small drawing, the same general method may be used for laying out elliptical shapes of any size.

To follow this procedure, you must first know how to locate the focus points. The distance between the two focus points is given by: $\sqrt{A^2 - B^2}$, where A is the major axis, and B is the minor axis. Set up for the calculator, this becomes:

Step 1. **Major Axis** $\boxed{x}$ $\boxed{=}$ Ans. 1

Step 2. **Minor Axis** $\boxed{x}$ $\boxed{=}$ $\boxed{x}$ $\boxed{-}$ 1 $\boxed{+}$ **Ans. 1** $\boxed{=}$ Ans. 2

Step 3. $\sqrt{\text{Ans. 2}}$ = Distance between focus points

This distance is laid out along the major axis equally on either side of the minor axis.

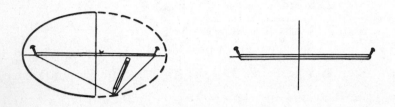

A pin is placed at each focus point, and a slack loop of thread or string is placed around the pins. When a pencil is used to draw the thread taut, as shown in the drawing, it will generate an ellipse as it is swung around the pins. To find the proper length for the thread or string, temporarily remove one pin from the focus point and place it at the end of the major axis. Knot the thread snugly around the two pins, then replace the pin at the focus point.

THE REGULAR POLYGON

There is a whole family of multisided figures in which the sides are all of equal length, and all joined by equal angles. The simplest of these is the equilateral triangle, and the next more complex is the familiar square, followed by the five-sided pentagon, and continuing with any desired number of sides:

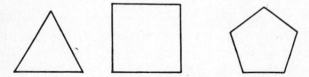

A regular polygon is drawn using a compass, protractor, and ruler. First draw a circle. Next, divide the 360° of the circle by the number of sides required, then use the protractor to mark the circumference of the circle with the numbers of degrees obtained. Connect the marks with straight lines and you have your polygon.

Calculating the area and various parts of a polygon is a moderately complex job, so we have done most of the work for you. As the following drawing shows, a circle can be inscribed within a polygon touching each side at its midpoint. The radius of such a circle is the same as the distance from the center of the polygon to the midpoint of a side. A circle can also be circumscribed around the outside. The result is that the radius of this circle is the same as the distance from the center to one of the angles.

Here is an illustration, together with definitions of the abbreviations being used:

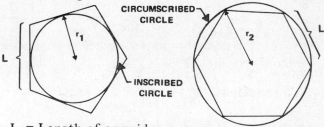

L = Length of one side

r_1 = (Read as "R sub-one") Distance from the center to the middle of one side. It is also the radius of the inscribed circle.

r_2 = Distance from the center to an apex between two sides. It is also the radius of the circumscribed circle.

A = Area of the polygon

We've prepared a table and a set of calculator procedures so that if you start with any sufficient information you can find all the other parts and the area of any polygon up to 12 sides. When a polygon has more than 12 sides, it approaches so closely to being a circle that the formulas for a circle can be used for most practical purposes.

This table gives the values for A, r_1, and r_2 when L has a value of 1.

POLYGON VALUES

Number of Sides	Name	A	r_1	r_2
3	Triangle	0.433	0.289	0.577
4	Square	1.000	0.500	0.707
5	Pentagon	1.720	0.688	0.851
6	Hexagon	2.598	0.866	1.000
7	Heptagon	3.634	1.038	1.152
8	Octagon	4.828	1.207	1.307
9	Nonagon	6.182	1.374	1.462
10	Decagon	7.694	1.539	1.618
11	Undecagon	9.366	1.703	1.775
12	Dodecagon	11.196	1.866	1.932

Calculator Formulas

1. If the length, L, of one side is known, the total area of the polygon is:

   L ⨯ **L** ⨯ **A (from table)** = Area

2. If the length, L, of a side is known, the distance from the center to the midpoint of an edge is:

   L ⨯ **r_1 (from table)** = Radius of inscribed circle

3. If the length, L, of a side is known, the distance from the center to an apex is:

    L $\boxed{\times}$ r_2 **(from table)** $\boxed{=}$ Radius of circumscribed circle

4. If the distance, r_1, from the center to the midpoint of a side is known, then the length of the side is:

    (Known) r_1 $\boxed{\div}$ r_1 **(from table)** $\boxed{=}$ Length of a side

    With the length of a side known, the area can now be calculated, using Formula 1.

5. If the distance, r_2, from the center to an apex is known, the length of a side is:

    (Known) r_2 $\boxed{\div}$ r_2 **(from table)** $\boxed{=}$ Length of a side

    With the length of a side known, the area can now be calculated, using Formula 1.

    (Note: The above procedures are calculator translations of standard formulas.)

ODD AND UNUSUAL SHAPES

It is often possible to find the area of odd or unusual shapes by dissecting them into several simple shapes. Problems of this sort are a great favorite in aptitude tests, and are often seen in College Board examinations or Civil Service tests, and similar problems sometimes arise in real life as well.

Here are several examples of the kind of thinking necessary to solve such problems.

A rhombus, the familiar diamond shape, is actually a special case of the parallelogram in which all four sides are of equal length. Its area can be found when only the diagonals are given, without any need to solve triangles. The rhombus can be reformed mentally into a rectangle, whereupon one diagonal becomes the width, and half the other diagonal becomes the height.

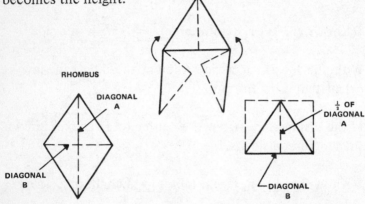

Therefore the area is $\frac{1}{2} \times A \times B$, or, set up for the calculator:

Diagonal A $\boxed{\times}$ **Diagonal B** $\boxed{\div}$ 2 $\boxed{=}$ **Area**

This Star of David is actually six rhombuses arranged in a circle·

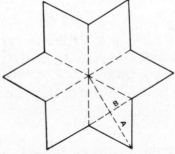

Using the formula previously given for the rhombus,

$$\frac{\text{Diagonal A} \times \text{Diagonal B}}{2},$$

then multiplying the result by 6, we quickly and easily find the area of this seemingly complex shape.

The graceful quatrefoil, often used in church windows, dissects into a square and four semicircles.

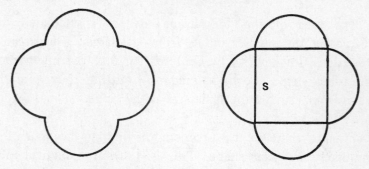

The one-step calculator procedure for the area of the entire quatrefoil, given the length, S, of the side of the contained square, is:

$$\pi \boxed{\div} 2 \boxed{+} 1 \boxed{\times} S \boxed{\times} S \boxed{=} \text{Area}$$

Since you will probably never have to figure the area of a quatrefoil in your entire life, we'll leave you the puzzle of how the calculator procedure was derived.

Another kind of area problem can be solved by subtracting one simple shape from another:

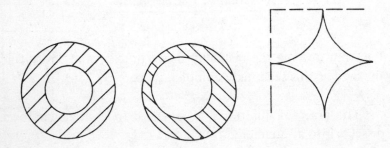

The area of the "doughnut" shape is calculated by subtracting the smaller circle from the larger. The smaller circle does not have to be centered for this to remain true. The other shape shown is made by cutting four quarter-circles from a square the same size as the circle.

Finally, there is the problem of finding the area of a completely irregular shape. This is a strictly practical job, done by estimating. The simplest procedure is to trace the shape onto a piece of graph paper, then count the squares covered by the shape. When a square is less than half filled, ignore it; when it is more than half filled, count it as a full square. Large blocks of squares can be more quickly counted by bounding them with rectangles, and multiplying length by width for these portions.

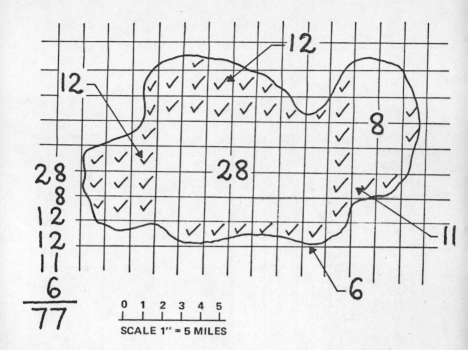

SCALE 1" = 5 MILES

Once the squares are counted, however, there still remains the problem of translating this raw count into actual square feet, square miles, or whatever unit is being used.

In the tracing of the lake shown in the illustration, the map was made on a scale of 1 inch = 5 miles. The graph paper was made with quarter-inch squares. Therefore each square on the graph paper was 1.25 miles by 1.25 miles, and had an area of 1.5625 square miles. Since the lake occupied about 77 squares, the lake had an area of 77 × 1.5625 = 120.3 square miles.

CHAPTER 9
VOLUMES, CAPACITIES, AND WEIGHTS

The ability to easily calculate the volume of various shapes, and to determine their weight or capacity allows the quick solution of many problems that most people wouldn't normally even bother to tackle. In the next few pages, we will show you how to handle these problems.

1) How much will that larger aquarium weigh, and will the bookshelf hold it?
2) How long will it take to fill the children's new swimming pool with the garden hose?
3) How big must a concrete block boat mooring be to weigh 100 pounds underwater?
4) How many bricks and how much sand base will be needed to make a brick terrace?

A few basic formulas and facts, plus the ability of the calculator to quickly handle the arithmetic, make these problems easy to solve. Even if you're not interested right now, we suggest you read quickly through this chapter so you'll know where to refer if a problem does arise.

RECTANGULAR BOXES (PARALLELEPIPED)

Volume is stated in cubic inches or cubic feet, or even in cubic yards in the case of sand or earth-moving. To someone unaccustomed to dealing with volumes, it is often surprising how large the numbers become. The question of the capacity of a suitcase in cubic inches is the same as the question: How many 1-inch blocks would the suitcase hold? The number is obviously very large. Let's look at a cubic foot compared to a cubic inch.

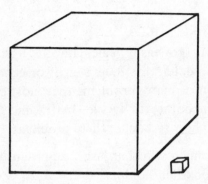

To compute the volume of an object, the first step is to obtain the area of the base, or the number of cubic units in the bottom layer.

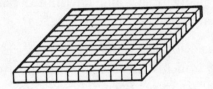

For a one-foot cube, this would be 12 × 12, or 144 units. To make a cubic foot, 12 such layers would be needed; thus, a cubic foot contains:

$$12 \times 12 \times 12 = 1728 \text{ (cubic inches)}$$

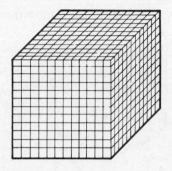

This same procedure is followed to determine the cubic contents of any box-shaped object, so we have:

Volume of a Parallelepiped (Flat-Sided Box)

Length ☒ Width ☒ Height ▣ Volume

THE CYLINDER

Another very common shape is the cylinder. It appears as all sorts of tanks, cans, containers, and utensils. The method of calculating the volume follows the same basic approach of: Area of Base × Height. In this case, however, the base is a circle, and finding its area requires the familiar formula, πr^2. It is often more convenient, however, to measure the diameter. Remember, to obtain the radius, divide the diameter by 2.

Volume of a Cylinder

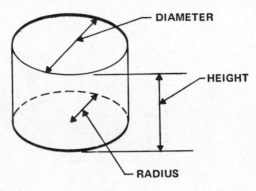

$$\pi r^2 h = \text{Volume}$$

Radius ⌐x⌐ ⌐=⌐ x 3.14 x Height = Volume

or

Diameter ÷ 2 ⌐x⌐ ⌐=⌐ x 3.14 x Height = Volume

THE PRISM

Rectangular and cylindrical objects constitute the majority of the shapes encountered, but there are several others that are occasionally needed. One of these shapes is a prism.

A good example of a prism is the shape of a typical attic. Its area is found by mentally standing it on end, calculating the area of the triangular base, and then multiplying by the height.

Volume of a Prism

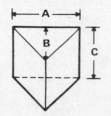

A $\boxed{\times}$ B $\boxed{\div}$ 2 $\boxed{\times}$ C $\boxed{=}$ Volume

THE PYRAMID AND CONE

A pyramid and a cone have similar formulas, both require that the area of the base be calculated first.

Volumes of Pyramids and Cones

 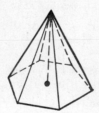 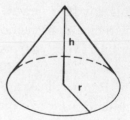

Area of Base $\boxed{\times}$ Height $\boxed{\div}$ 3 $\boxed{=}$ Volume

THE SPHERE

And finally, the volume of the familiar ball shape or spherical shape can be calculated using the formula:

Volume of a Sphere

$$\frac{4}{3}\,\pi r^3 = \text{Volume}$$

Since it is far easier to measure the diameter, this calculator procedure is set up for diameter:

(CONST) Diameter $\div$ 2 $\boxed{\times}$ $\boxed{=}$ $\boxed{=}$ $\times$ 3.14 $\boxed{\times}$ 4 $\boxed{\div}$ 3 $\boxed{=}$ Volume

In trying to find the volume of a complex or unusual shape, a good approximation can often be made by treating it as a simpler shape, or as a combination of simple shapes. In this kind of practical approach, you are not striving for mathematic perfection, but only for the accuracy needed for ordinary, everyday use.

For instance, the traditional coffee cup or tea cup is very close to being half of a sphere:

Using the calculator procedure just given, we have:

(CONST) 3.75 $\boxed{\div}$ 2 $\boxed{\times}$ $\boxed{=}$ $\boxed{=}$ $\boxed{\times}$ 3.14 $\boxed{\times}$ 4 $\boxed{\div}$ 3 $\boxed{=}$ 27.597654

This is the volume of the entire sphere; half of it is:

27.597654 $\boxed{\div}$ 2 $\boxed{=}$ 13.798827 (or 14 cubic inches)

The proper way to figure the volume of a flower pot is to extend it to form an imaginary cone, compute the volume of the entire cone, subtract from it the volume of the imaginary addition, leaving the volume of the flower pot. However, it is much easier, and almost as accurate to calculate one cylinder using the top of the flower pot as a "base" and another using the bottom as a base, then taking the average of these two bases.

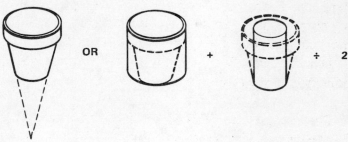

OR

+ ÷ 2

Practical considerations should always be kept in mind. For example, a large box used to store sand or similar materials is sometimes shaped like this:

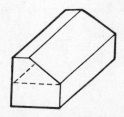

Its total internal volume is a little complicated to figure, but is not needed. In use, the box is only filled to the level of the front edge and this determines its working capacity.

The usual purpose of measuring volumes is to either determine the liquid capacity of a shape, or to find its weight. To do these, you need to know how to translate cubic volume to liquid measure, and you need to know the weights of various substances:

A cubic foot contains 1728 cubic inches.

A cubic foot holds 7.5 gallons or 30 quarts.

A pint contains 29 cubic inches.

Water weighs 62.5 pounds per cubic foot, or 8.3 pounds per gallon.

WEIGHTS OF SOME COMMON SUBSTANCES

The following table gives the approximate weight of a cubic foot (1728 cubic inches) of the substances listed.

Substance	Approximate weight in pounds per cubic foot
Aluminum	162
Books	30 to 40
Brass	500 to 525
Brick, common	125
Charcoal	15 to 30
Clothing, firmly packed	10 to 15
Concrete	145
Copper	540 to 555
Cork	15
Earth, moist, loose	70 to 80
Gasoline, kerosene, etc.	45 to 50
Glass	160 to 180
Gold	1204
Ice	57
Iron, cast	450
Lead	710
Mud	110 to 130
Oils, vegetable or mineral	55 to 60
Sand	90 to 120
Silver	655
Snow, fresh fallen	5 to 12
Snow, wet and compacted	15 to 50
Steel	490
Stone, unbroken	160 (varies with type)
*Water	62.5
Wood, hard	45 ⎰ varies widely with type
Wood, soft	30 ⎱ and moisture content

*Use the weight of water for all water-like substances, such as canned vegetables, fruit juice, beverages or milk.

SOME PRACTICE PROBLEMS

Let's use this information to solve some problems, and demonstrate the ease with which answers can be obtained.

The Aquarium

You propose to buy a new aquarium which weighs about 20 pounds empty and is 24 inches long, 9 inches deep, and will be filled to a depth of 12 inches. What will it weigh when it is full?

The volume of water is obtained by multiplying the three dimensions together:

$$24 \boxed{\times} 9 \boxed{\times} 12 \boxed{=} 2592 \text{ (cubic inches)}$$

There are 1728 cubic inches in a cubic foot, so to convert this result to cubic feet we do:

$$2592 \boxed{\div} 1728 \boxed{=} 1.5 \text{ (cubic feet)}$$

Water weighs 62.5 pounds per cubic foot, so the next step is:

$$1.5 \boxed{\times} 62.5 \boxed{=} 93.75 \text{ (pounds)}$$

We have the weight of the water, and we knew the empty aquarium was 20 pounds, so we have a total weight of 114 pounds. The shelf on which it will stand had better be sturdy.

The Swimming Pool

You have bought an above-ground plastic-lined swimming pool. It is 15 feet by 9 feet by 3 feet deep. How long will it take to fill with the garden hose?

You find that the hose will fill a discarded half-gallon milk container in 10 seconds; therefore one gallon takes 20 seconds, and 3 gallons will flow per minute.

The volume of the swimming pool is:

15 $\boxed{\times}$ 9 $\boxed{\times}$ 3 $\boxed{=}$ 405 (cubic feet)

Since there are 7.5 gallons per cubic foot, the pool will hold:

405 $\boxed{\times}$ 7.5 $\boxed{=}$ 3037.5 (gallons)

We had determined that the hose delivers 3 gallons per minute, so it will take 1000 minutes to fill the 3000-gallon pool. Therefore 1000 minutes is:

1000 $\boxed{\div}$ 60 $\boxed{=}$ 16.6 (hours)

The Concrete Boat Mooring

You have been told that you should have a 100-pound mooring for your boat, so you propose to cast one using some ready-mix concrete. How big should it be? The chart says that concrete weighs 145 pounds per cubic foot, so the size of the block should be:

100 $\boxed{\div}$ 145 $\boxed{=}$ .6896551 (or .7 cubic foot)

This would indicate a piece of concrete 12 inches by 12 inches by 8.5 inches. Your boat goes ashore in the next storm, pulling the mooring with it. What went wrong?

Things put in the water try to float, and their effective weight is reduced by the weight of the water they displace. A cubic foot of wood weighing 45 pounds will sink until it has displaced 45 pounds of water, then it will remain stable.

Our 100 pound block of concrete, with its volume of .7 of a cubic foot, displaced .7 of a cubic foot of water weighing about 44 pounds. Thus, underwater, the 100-pound piece of concrete weighed only 56 pounds.

We should have begun the problem by recognizing that concrete weighs 145 pounds per cubic foot, and water weighs 62.5 pounds, therefore the weight of concrete, underwater, is:

$$145 \boxed{-} 62.5 \boxed{=} 82.5 \text{ (pounds per cubic foot)}$$

To obtain 100 pounds on the bottom, we need:

$$100 \boxed{\div} 82.5 \boxed{=} 1.2 \text{ (cubic feet)}$$

This is almost double our original figure.

The Terrace

You are considering making a terrace at the back of your house, 12 feet by 15 feet, and made of bricks laid in sand. You've been advised to have a 3-inch layer of sand beneath the bricks. You're going to have to move all the materials by wheelbarrow from the front of the house to the back. You'd like some idea of how much work is involved, as well as needing to know the amount of brick and sand to order.

Let's first figure the volume of sand. Dimensions in feet are: 12 by 15 by .25 (that is, 3 inches)

$$12 \boxed{\times} 15 \boxed{\times} .25 \boxed{=} 45 \text{ (cubic feet of sand)}$$

Sand is normally sold by the cubic yard which contains 27 cubic feet. Thus, 2 yards will be just a little over your requirement. How much will this weigh? Our chart lists sand as weighing 90 to 120 pounds per cubic foot. Let's select 100 pounds as the value for estimating. Furthermore, we figure on being able to handle 60 pounds per trip in the wheelbarrow. The number of wheelbarrow trips is:

$$54 \text{ (cubic feet)} \boxed{\times} 100 \boxed{\div} 60 \boxed{=} 90 \text{ (trips)}$$

That's a little upsetting. You could put more in the wheelbarrow, but there's a nasty little uphill stretch that would be difficult.

Let's look at the bricks. A brick measures $3\frac{1}{2} \times 8$ inches, so the area is:

$$3.5 \boxed{\times} 8 \boxed{=} 28 \text{ (square inches)}$$

The terrace is to be 12 feet by 15 feet. There are 144 square inches in a square foot, so the terrace in square inches is:

$$12 \boxed{\times} 15 \boxed{\times} 144 \boxed{=} 25920$$

The number of bricks needed is:

$$25920 \;\boxed{\div}\; 28 \;\boxed{=}\; 925$$

In view of those 90 trips with the sand, we'd better check out the bricks. The chart in this book shows that bricks weigh 130 pounds per cubic foot. The volume of one brick is:

$$3.5 \;\boxed{\times}\; 8 \;\boxed{\times}\; 2.25 \;\boxed{=}\; 63 \text{ (cubic inches)}$$

Since there are 1728 cubic inches in a cubic foot, we can find bricks per cubic foot by:

$$1728 \;\boxed{\div}\; 63 \;\boxed{=}\; 27.4 \text{ (bricks per cubic foot)}$$

If 27.5 bricks weigh 130 pounds, one brick weighs:

$$130 \;\boxed{\div}\; 27.4 \;\boxed{=}\; 4.7445255 \text{ (pounds)}$$

Multiply this by the 1,000 bricks needed and:

$$4.7445255 \;\boxed{\times}\; 1000 \;\boxed{=}\; 4744 \text{ (pounds of brick)}$$

At the rate of 60 pounds per wheelbarrow trip, this is:

$$4744 \;\boxed{\div}\; 60 \;\boxed{=}\; 79 \text{ (wheelbarrow trips)}$$

You now have some solid information about the materials and effort required to build your terrace, and can make a proper decision as to whether you should proceed. Furthermore, if you decide to hire someone else to do it, you have a better basis for judging the fairness of the price.

SPECIFIC GRAVITY

If the specific gravity of a substance is known, this figure can easily be translated into its weight for a certain volume. Specific gravity values are often much easier to find than other references to weight; even a dictionary lists the specific gravity of the pure elements.

Specific gravity is the weight of a certain volume of a substance compared with the same volume of water. For instance, tin has a specific gravity of 7.3. Therefore a cubic foot of tin would weigh 7.3 times as much as a cubic foot of water. Since water weighs 62.5 pounds per cubic foot, tin must weigh:

$$62.5 \times 7.3 = 456.25 \text{ (pounds per cubic foot)}$$

Substances which are lighter than water will have a specific gravity of less than 1. Ice, for instance, has a specific gravity of .92; therefore a cubic foot of ice would weigh:

$$62.5 \times .92 = 57.5 \text{ (pounds per cubic foot)}$$

It follows, then, that materials with a specific gravity of less than 1 will float on water.

THE METRIC SYSTEM

The metric system was first suggested in 1670, and was formalized in 1790. Since that time, it has made continual progress against various other systems of weights and measures, especially in Europe.

Quick Reference Chart

This chart gives the approximate values and the calculator procedures for the most-used metric conversions. Insert the known term in the proper place at the left side, perform the operation indicated and obtain the result shown at the right.

▭	Centimeters	÷ 2.54	= ___	Inches
▭	Degrees Centigrade	× 1.8 + 32	= ___	Degrees Fahrenheit
▭	Degrees Fahrenheit	− 32 ÷ 1.8	= ___	Degrees Centigrade
▭	Feet	÷ 3.28	= ___	Meters
▭	Gallons	× 3.79	= ___	Liters
▭	Inches	× 2.54	= ___	Centimeters
▭	Inches	× 25.4	= ___	Millimeters
▭	Kilograms	× 2.2	= ___	Pounds
▭	Kilometers	÷ 1.61	= ___	Miles
▭	Liters	÷ 3.79	= ___	Gallons
▭	Liters	× 1.06	= ___	Quarts
▭	Meters	× 3.28	= ___	Feet
▭	Miles	× 1.61	= ___	Kilometers
▭	Millimeters	÷ 25.4	= ___	Inches
▭	Pounds	÷ 2.2	= ___	Kilograms
▭	Quarts	÷ 1.06	= ___	Liters

Although the metric system has long been the legal basis for weights and measures in the United States, its use has never been required. It has had wide acceptance only in scientific areas. It seems inevitable that the world will have to adopt a uniform system at some time, however.

The metric system is very logical and easy to understand. Its units are related to each other by multiples of ten. Thus most conversions merely involve moving the decimal point, rather than, for example, going through the complex arithmetic necessary to convert inches to feet to yards to miles.

The basic unit of length is the *meter*. It is very similar to the yard, and is used where we would use feet or yards.

The prefixes to the names of the units tell how much to multiply or divide the basic unit. Thus, a kilometer is a 1000 meters because *kilo* means 1000. Similarly, a kilogram is 1000 grams. The widely used prefixes are:

milli	1/1000
centi	1/100
hecto	100 times
kilo	1000 times

The *kilometer* is 1000 meters and is used instead of miles. A kilometer is .62 mile, or about $\frac{5}{8}$ of a mile.

The *centimeter* is $\frac{1}{100}$ of a meter and is used for "inch range" distances. It is .39 inch, or about $\frac{3}{8}$ of an inch.

The *millimeter* is used for fine measurements. There are 25.4 millimeters to an inch, so a millimeter is about .040 inch.

The *liter*, a measure of volume, is 1000 cubic centimeters. It is very close to a quart in size, and there are 1.06 quarts to the liter.

The *kilogram*, a unit of weight (technically, mass), was supposed to have been the weight of a liter of water at 4°C. It weighs 2.2 pounds. The kilogram is popularly referred to as a kilo.

The *gram* is the unit for small weights. A dime weighs about 2 grams. There are about 28.35 grams to an ounce.

The *metric ton* is at the opposite end of the weight scale. It is 1000 kilograms, or approximately 2205 pounds, so it is about 10% heavier than the common (or short) ton.

Temperature is measured in *degrees Centigrade*, abbreviated as 40°C, or merely as 40 C. This scale uses the freezing point of water as 0° and water's boiling point as 100°. The designation *Centigrade* was recently changed to *Celsius* in honor of the 18th century Swedish astronomer, but the older designation is still widely used.

A complete list of exact metric conversions will be found in Appendix I.

CHAPTER 10
INTEREST

In a free society, money flows to the place where it will have its most productive use, moving back and forth between those who have earned more than they have spent, and those who need capital for business purposes or wish to borrow money for their personal needs. *Interest* is the fee paid for the use of money.

The basic rules governing interest are few and simple. However, the arithmetic is sometimes lengthy and tedious. The calculator can remove most of this burden. It can make it easy to determine exactly what is being spent on interest and finance charges so that *informed* decisions may be made.

All discussion of interest should be reduced to a true *annual interest rate* so that there is an understandable basis for comparison. To do this, only three pieces of information are needed:

How much was I in debt?
How long was I in debt?
What did it cost me to be in debt?

The answer to this last question of cost should include *any* costs that would not have been incurred if there had been no indebtedness. This is the case whether the cost is called interest, revolving credit charge, service charge, or even the required life insurance on a loan. To find the annual rate of interest being paid requires only two calculator procedures:

Cost of debt $\boxed{\div}$ Amount of debt $\boxed{\times}$ 100 $\boxed{=}$ % Interest

If the debt existed for one year, then this answer is the annual interest rate. If the debt was for a period different than a year, adjust it this way:

12 $\boxed{\div}$ Time in months $\boxed{\times}$ % Interest $\boxed{=}$ Annual interest rate

Let's work an example. An $88.95 purchase is made at a department store on January 15 and charged. The bill is received at the end of January for the net amount, but is not paid. A month later a second bill is received for $88.95 plus $1.34 carrying charge, and still is not paid. At the end of March, a third bill is received for $88.95, plus $2.70 carrying charge, and a $3.50 late payment penalty, together with a brisk note. Finally on April 15, the bill was paid. What was the annual interest rate?

Using the first procedure, we have:

2.70 $\boxed{+}$ 3.50 $\boxed{\div}$ 88.95 $\boxed{\times}$ 100 $\boxed{=}$ 6.97 (%)

The store's money was "borrowed" for three months. To convert the 6.97% to an annual rate, we have:

12 $\boxed{\div}$ 3 $\boxed{\times}$ 6.97 $\boxed{=}$ 27.88 or 28% annual interest.

INSTALLMENT LOANS

An installment loan is the arrangement in which a sum of money is borrowed, and then repaid in equal installments over a period of time, typically 12 to 36 months. These loans are frequently used to purchase automobiles, to borrow money for vacations, or to pay for unusual expenses. Interest rates on such loans vary widely.

Let us consider another example. You want to buy a used car and need $960. You find the bank will lend you this sum at a rate of 5.25%, *discounted*. You agree to repay the loan in 12 monthly installments of $85 each. These payments include the repayment of principal, the interest charges, and $3.88 for life insurance to pay off the balance of the loan in the event of your death.

The following is the way the bank arrived at the above payment schedule. You may want to follow the procedure on your own calculator.

The *face* amount of the loan is the same as the sum of the payments:

85 (dollars) $\boxed{\times}$ **12 (payments)** $\boxed{=}$ 1020 (dollars)

Since the loan will be for one year at the rate of 5.25%, the interest charge will be:

1020 $\boxed{\times}$ **5.25** $\boxed{\div}$ **100** $\boxed{=}$ 53.55

To this must be added the $3.88 insurance charge:

53.55 $\boxed{+}$ **3.88** $\boxed{=}$ 57.43

This amount is now deducted from the face amount of the loan, and you are handed a check for the balance:

1020 $\boxed{-}$ **57.43** $\boxed{=}$ 962.57

Now, you will be repaying this amount steadily over the next twelve months. On the average, you will have the use of a little more than half of it. Also, you are paying interest on the entire $1020, but you will have the use of no more than $962.57. These factors work out so that *the true annual percentage rate is approximately twice the nominal rate.*

There are several methods that can be used to estimate the true annual interest rate – yielding slightly different answers. Here are two that seem easy to use.

In detail, if we start with $1020 then our 12 monthly balances are:

$$
\begin{array}{r}
1020 \\
935 \\
850 \\
765 \\
680 \\
595 \\
510 \\
425 \\
340 \\
255 \\
170 \\
\underline{85} \\
6630
\end{array}
$$

In this case, we see that the average monthly balance is $6630 \div 12 = 552.5$. Therefore, an estimated annual interest rate is $57.43 \div 552.5$ or 10.4%.

A slightly different method uses the average time period in months. In this case, since we pay at the end of the 1st month and 12th month, we have an average of $\frac{1 + 12}{2} = \frac{13}{2}$ months or $\frac{13}{2} \div 12 = \frac{13}{24}$ years. Now our unpaid balance is 962.57, and the cost of carrying it is $57.43 for this time period. Now we use the fact that interest is the product of rate times the time in years times the principal: $I = p \times r \times t$. Hence,

$$r = \frac{I}{p \times t} = \frac{57.43}{962.57 \times \dfrac{13}{24}}$$

In calculator notation, this becomes

$$57.43 \boxed{\times} 24 \boxed{\div} 962.57 \boxed{\div} 13 \boxed{=} .11$$

or 11%.

Because of the installment repayment method, you have the use of all the money the first month, that is twelve 12ths. You then have eleven 12ths the second month, ten 12ths the third month, and so on. Notice that if we add these fractions together we get a total of seventy-eight 12ths. The lender, on the other hand, earns twelve 78ths of his money the first month, eleven 78ths the second month, and continuing until he earns only one 78th in the last month. If you wish to repay the loan two months early, you are entitled to a credit of only three 78ths of the interest you have paid. The bank earns half of its interest in the first $3 \frac{1}{2}$ months of the loan! (This is sometimes known as the rule of 78s.)

The term of a loan has a major impact on interest cost. If the $960 loan we have been discussing is set up for a 30-month period, the interest cost would increase. Here are the calculator procedures for installment loans, using this new loan as an example.

First we need to know what the total percent interest would be for the entire loan:

Time (in months) $\boxed{\div}$ 12 $\boxed{\times}$ Annual interest rate $\boxed{=}$ Total % interest.

In this case,

$$30 \text{ (months)} \boxed{\div} 12 \boxed{\times} 5.25 \text{ (\%)} \boxed{=} 13.125 \text{ (\%)}$$

When the desired net proceeds are known and the total percent interest is known, the face amount can be found with this procedure:

(CONST) 100 $\boxed{-}$ % interest $\boxed{\div}$ Net proceeds $\boxed{\div}$ $\boxed{=}$ $\boxed{=}$
$\boxed{\times}$ 100 $\boxed{=}$ Face amount.

That is,

(CONST) 100 $\boxed{-}$ 13.125 $\boxed{\div}$ 960 $\boxed{\div}$ $\boxed{=}$ $\boxed{=}$
$\boxed{\times}$ 100 $\boxed{=}$ 1105.037

Thus, $1105.037 is the face amount of the loan. But when we divide this by 30 payments (do it), the result is $36.83 $\frac{1}{3}$ per month. Since it's better for everyone to have even dollar amounts, we'll make the payments $37 per month, times 30 months equals $1110, the final face amount. We now need to find the exact net proceeds. Here is the procedure:

Annual interest rate $\div$ 12 $\times$ Time (in months) $\times$ Face amount $\div$ 100 $=$ Amount of interest

or

5.25 $\div$ 12 $\times$ 30 $\times$ 1110 $\div$ 100 $=$ 145.6875 (dollars)

This interest charge must be deducted from the face amount to find the net proceeds, that is, the amount actually given to the borrower:

1110 $-$ 145.69 $=$ 964:31

By borrowing the same amount, but repaying it in 30 months instead of 12 months, we have *increased* the interest cost by $92.14 on a $964.31 loan!

HOME MORTGAGE

A home mortgage is essentially a gigantic installment purchase. Let's take a brief look at a typical mortgage. This one was for $14,200, for 25 years, at the rate of 5.5%, with monthly payments of $87.21. (This happened some years ago!)

The first month this mortgage is in effect, the borrower owes $14,200. At the end of the month, he must pay interest at the rate of one-twelfth of the annual rate:

14200 $\times$ 5.5 $\div$ 12 $\div$ 100 $=$ 65.08

However, his monthly payments are \$87.21. Subtracting the \$65.08 interest leaves \$22.13, which goes towards reducing the principal. As a result, during the next months he owes:

$$14200 \; \boxed{-} \; 22.13 \; \boxed{=} \; 14177.87$$

The interest charge on this is:

$$14177.87 \; \boxed{\times} \; 5.5 \; \boxed{\div} \; 12 \; \boxed{\div} \; 100 \; \boxed{=} \; 64.98$$

So, in the second month his interest cost was 10¢ less, and the reduction of the principal was 10¢ more.

Let's look at just a sample of the payments for this mortgage, picking the first payment made at five-year intervals:

Payment Number	Amount of Payment	Amount Applied to		Remaining Balance
		Interest	Principal	
				14,200.00
1	87.21	65.08	22.13	14,177.87
60	87.21	58.23	28.98	12,675.85
120	87.21	49.08	38.13	10,670.54
180	87.21	37.04	50.17	8,032.15
240	87.21	21.21	66.00	4,560.85
299	87.21	.77	86.44	80.47

Computing such schedules is beyond the scope of this book and is an extremely tedious job. However, The Financial Publishing Co., 82 Brookline Ave., Boston, Mass. 02215 will prepare an individual amortization schedule showing the amount applied to principal and interest, and the remaining balance, for every month of your mortgage. They need to know the amount of the original loan, the number of years, the monthly payment, and the rate of interest. Their charge is only $1.00, and this payment should be included with your request.

The same company publishes two booklets containing summaries of this kind of information for a wide range of interest rates and terms:

Booklet 193 is for mortgages from 6% to 12%, up to $75,000

Booklet 392 is for 7% to 18%, up to $100,000.
Either booklet is $2.00.

EARNED INTEREST

Receiving interest is a good deal more pleasant to think about than paying interest. Most people's experience with interest has been in connection with savings accounts, so let's discuss these.

Different types of banks offer different rates, and even within one bank several savings plans at various rates of interest will be available. How are decisions made about the most advantageous way to save one's money? It costs the bank money to handle your account, so they can afford to pay a little extra interest if you choose a method of savings which minimizes their paperwork.

The usual form of savings account pays interest on the money in your account at the end of each quarter. If you deposit money on January 30 and leave it in the account until the end of March (that is, the end of the first quarter), the bank will pay you two month's interest. But if you withdraw it on March 15, you lose all your interest for that quarter.

How meaningful are small differences in interest rates? Let's say you have $800 in the bank located in the same block where you work, and that you try to deposit another $25 each payday. The bank pays $5\frac{1}{2}$ interest, but another bank, half a mile away, pays 6%.

Bank 1: **800** $\boxed{\times}$ **.055** $\boxed{=}$ 44 (dollars interest)

Bank 2: **800** $\boxed{\times}$ **.06** $\boxed{=}$ 48 (dollars interest)

You'd be ahead about $4 a year in Bank 2. This is not a very large amount but on the other hand, if you had several thousand dollars in long-term savings, it could make quite a bit of difference. Try this as an exercise on a calculator.

The compounding of interest in savings accounts is a subject which is both fascinating and confusing. The calculator can solve compound interest problems and also offers a good insight into these problems.

To see how compounding works, let's look at an imaginary situation in which someone opened an account with $1.00, and left it on deposit for a year in a bank paying 6%, compounded quarterly.

At the end of the first quarter-year, the bank would credit this account with $1\frac{1}{2}$% interest, which is one-fourth of the 6% annual rate. We'll show $1\frac{1}{2}$% as .015. To determine the interest, they would multiply the principal of one dollar by the rate of .015:

$$1 \boxed{\times} .015 \boxed{=} .015 \text{ (dollars, or } 1\frac{1}{2}\cancel{c})$$

They now must add the $1\frac{1}{2}\cancel{c}$ to the dollar on deposit:

$$1 \boxed{+} .015 \boxed{=} 1.015$$

However, they could have saved a step in this calculation. Their final figure consisted of 100% of the amount on deposit plus $1 \frac{1}{2}\%$ of the amount on deposit, or $101 \frac{1}{2}\%$ of the amount on deposit. They could have done the following to obtain the same result.

$$1 \text{ (dollar) } \boxed{\times} \; 1.015 \; (101 \tfrac{1}{2}\%) \; \boxed{=} \; 1.015 \; (\$1.01 \tfrac{1}{2})$$

At the end of the second quarter, the new principal amount of 1.015 should be multiplied by $101 \frac{1}{2}\%$ again:

$$1.015 \; \boxed{\times} \; 1.015 \; \boxed{=} \; 1.030225$$

At the end of the third quarter, this latest principal amount is again multiplied by 1.015:

$$1.030225 \; \boxed{\times} \; 1.015 \; \boxed{=} \; 1.0456783$$

And again at the end of the fourth quarter:

$$1.0456783 \; \boxed{\times} \; 1.015 \; \boxed{=} \; 1.0613634$$

Thus, the \$1.00 has not only earned 6¢ in interest due to the 6% interest rate, but has also earned $\frac{13634}{100000}$ of a cent due to compounding (that is, \$.0013634).

But let's look again at the arithmetic it took to arrive at the year-end result. All we really did was:

$$1 \; \boxed{\times} \; 1.015 \; \boxed{\times} \; 1.015 \; \boxed{\times} \; 1.015 \; \boxed{\times} \; 1.015 \; \boxed{=} \; 1.0613634$$

The 1 at the beginning contributes nothing, and we can multiply a number by itself by using the Constant mode:

(CONST) **1.015** $\boxed{\times}$ $\boxed{=}$ $\boxed{=}$ $\boxed{=}$ 1.0613634

Thus, to calculate compound interest, the annual interest rate is divided by the number of periods. If interest is compounded quarterly, there are four periods per year; if it is compounded monthly, there are twelve periods per year. To this result is added the whole number 1. Then, with the calculator in Constant mode, press the $\boxed{\times}$ key, and then press the $\boxed{=}$ key *one less time* than the total number of periods.

This procedure will give the result for a $1.00 deposit. If the result is wanted for a different amount, merely multiply the final result by this different amount.

Let's find out what the difference would be for $1500 for 5 years in an account compounded annually, and one compounded quarterly, both at 6% interest.

For the account compounded annually, there are five periods at the rate of .06, to which we must add the dollar:

1 $\boxed{+}$ **.06** $\boxed{=}$ 1.06

This is now raised to the 5th power, which requires operating the equal key *four* times:

(CONST) **1.06** $\boxed{\times}$ $\boxed{=}$ $\boxed{=}$ $\boxed{=}$ $\boxed{=}$ 1.3382255

This is the amount earned by one dollar, and we are working on $1500, so that result is multiplied by 1500:

1.3382255 $\boxed{\times}$ 1500 $\boxed{=}$ 2007.3382 (or $2007.34)

Solving the same problem, except with interest rate compounded quarterly, requires first finding the interest rate for one quarter.

.06 $\boxed{\div}$ 4 $\boxed{=}$ .015 (or 1.5% per quarter)

In five years there are twenty quarters, so we must raise 1.015 to the 20th power:

1.015 $\boxed{\times}$ **(operate** $\boxed{=}$ **key 19 times)** 1.3468538

This is the amount for $1.00, so we must multiply by 1500:

1.3468538 $\boxed{\times}$ **1500** $\boxed{=}$ 2020.2807 (or $2020.28)

This result compares to $2007.34 when compounded annually, so the quarterly compounding earned an additional $12.94!

It is fascinating to watch how the growth of a compound interest account accelerates with time. Let's take an entirely fictitious tale of a young man who was given $1000 by a rich aunt on his 21st birthday, with the request that he save it until he is 65 years old. Because she died the next day, he felt obliged to honor her wish as a kind of deathbed request. He found a bank which would issue him a savings certificate, bearing interest compounded at 7% annually, and guaranteed for 44 years. Enter the following on the calculator:

(CONST) 1.07 $\boxed{\times}$ $\boxed{=}$ $\boxed{=}$ $\boxed{=}$ ...

The entry of 1.07 is the value of one dollar at the end of one year. The first operation of the $\boxed{=}$ key gives the value at the end of two years, so say, "two." Continue pressing the $\boxed{=}$ key and watch the display. The decimal point can be mentally moved three places to the right to account for the fact that the number in the display is to be multiplied by 1000, and you can watch the account grow year by year. It takes a little over ten years to grow by $1000. The next $1000 only takes 7 years. Finally, it is *growing* at the rate of $1000 per year.

Some banks now advertise interest compounded daily. How much real difference results from more frequent compounding? Here is a comparison of the interest earned at 6% on $1000 in one year compounded at various intervals:

Compounded annually	$60.00
quarterly	$61.36
monthly	$61.68
weekly	$61.80
daily	$61.83
continuously	$61.83 $\frac{6}{10}$

Legend says that Peter Minuet purchased Manhattan Island from the Indians in 1626 for $24 worth of bright cloth, beads, and trinkets. If the Indians had asked for cash instead, and had been able to deposit it in a bank paying 6% compounded quarterly (and if there were no rule against such perpetuities), by 1973 their account would have grown to $22,650,504,900. This $22 billion is not too far from the amount needed to buy Manhattan back, tear down the buildings, and restore the original forests.

APPENDIX I

HOW TO USE SOME COMMON MATHEMATICAL TABLES

COMMON ANTILOGARITHMS

L	0	1	2	3	4	5	6	7	8	9	Proportional parts 1	2	3	4	5
.15	1413	1416	1419	1422	1426	1429	1432	1435	1439	1442	0	1	1	1	2
.16	1445	1449	1452	1455	1459	1462	1466	1469	1472	1476	0	1	1	1	2
.17	1479	1483	1486	1489	1493	1496	1500	1503	1507	1510	0	1	1	1	2
.18	1514	1517	1521	1524	1528	1531	1535	1538	1542	1545	0	1	1	1	2
.19	1549	1552	1556	1560	1563	1567	1570	1574	1578	1581	0	1	1	1	2
.20	1585	1589	1592	1596	1600			1611	1614	1618	0	1	1	1	2
.21	1622	1626	1629	1633	1637		1652	1656	0	1	1	2	2
.22	1660	1663	1667	1671	1675		1690	1694	0	1	1	2	2
.23	1698	1702	1706	1710	1714		1730	1734	0	1	1	2	2
.24	1738	1742	1746	1750			1770	1774	0	1	1	2	2
.25	1778	1782	1786				1811	1816	0	1	1	2	2
.26	1820	1824					1858	0	1	1	2	2
.27	1862	1866				1901	0	1	1	2	2
.28	1905	1910		1919			0	1	1	2	2
.29	1950	1954		1963		1986	0	1	1	2	2
.30	1995	2000		2009		2032	0	1	1	2	2
.31	2042	2046		2056	2075	2099	0	1	1	2	2
.32	2089	2094			2123		0	1	1	2	2
.33	2138	2143			2173		1	1	2	2
.34	2188	2193			2223	2234	2	2	3
.35	2239	2244	2249	2254		2275	2286	1	1	2	2	3
.36	2291	2296	2301	2307		2328	2333	2339	1	1	2	2	3
.37	2344	2350	2355	2360		2382	2388	2393	1	1	2	2	3
.38	2399	2404	2410	2415		2438	2443	2449	1	1	2	2	3
.39	2455	2460	2466	2472	2483	2495	2500	2506	1	1	2	2	3
1	0	1	2	3	5	7	8	9	1	2	3	4	5

Enter from the margins with the given (common) logarithm, the corresponding number is given in the body of the table.

APPENDIX I
HOW TO USE SOME
COMMON MATHEMATICAL TABLES

TABLES OF TRIGONOMETRIC FUNCTIONS

A full treatment of trigonometry is beyond the scope of this book. If you find the following basic formulas interesting and useful, a paperback Eleventh Year Mathematics review book will provide further valuable information. It is available in most school supply stores.

A triangle has six elements: three sides and three angles. If any three of these elements are known, it is possible to find the remaining three (except, that if only the angles are known, the triangle may be any size).

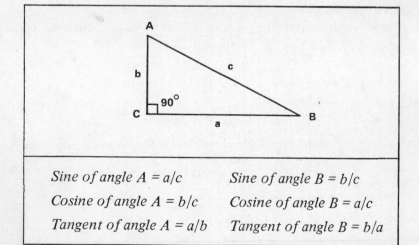

Sine of angle A = a/c	*Sine of angle B = b/c*
Cosine of angle A = b/c	*Cosine of angle B = a/c*
Tangent of angle A = a/b	*Tangent of angle B = b/a*

The sum of the angles of a triangle is always 180°. In a right triangle (meaning that angle C is 90°), the sum of the two remaining angles must be 90°, and if one of them is known, the other can be determined by subtracting from 90°.

If two of the sides, or one side and one angle (A or B) are known, the above formulas and the table will permit any remaining element to be found. Select the formula which includes the two known elements and the desired unknown element, and solve, using the table to find the value of the function.

Example: Given side a = 17 inches and side b = 33 inches. Find angle A.
Use formula: Tangent of angle A = a/b.
Substituting our known values, we obtain:

$$\frac{a}{b} = \frac{17}{33} = 17 \div 33 = .5152$$

In Tangent column find value closest to .5152 = 27°.

Example: Given side c = 57 feet and angle B = 19°. Find side a.
Use formula: Cosine of angle B = a/c.
Cosine of 19° (from table) = .9455.
Substituting, we have .9455 = a/57.
Therefore, a = 57 × .9455 = 53.9 feet.

AREA OF A TRIANGLE

For any triangle (not necessarily a right triangle), if two sides and the angle where they meet are known, the area can be found.

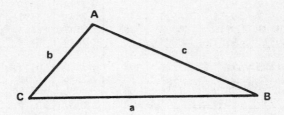

$$\text{Area} = \frac{a \times b \times \text{Sine} \angle C}{2} \text{ or } \frac{b \times c \times \text{Sine} \angle A}{2}$$

$$\text{or } \frac{a \times c \times \text{Sine} \angle B}{2}$$

Example: Given side b = 19 feet, side c = 23 feet and angle A = 40°

Find: Area of triangle

Sine 40° (from table) = .6428

$$\text{Area} = \frac{19 \times 23 \times .6428}{2} = 140.4518 \text{ square feet.}$$

Table of Natural Trigonometric Functions

Angle	Sine	Cosine	Tangent	Angle	Sine	Cosine	Tangent
1°	.0175	.9998	.0175	46°	.7193	.6947	1.0355
2°	.0349	.9994	.0349	47°	.7314	.6820	1.0724
3°	.0523	.9986	.0524	48°	.7431	.6691	1.1106
4°	.0698	.9976	.0699	49°	.7547	.6561	1.1504
5°	.0872	.9962	.0875	50°	.7660	.6428	1.1918
6°	.1045	.9945	.1051	51°	.7771	.6293	1.2349
7°	.1219	.9925	.1228	52°	.7880	.6157	1.2799
8°	.1392	.9903	.1405	53°	.7986	.6018	1.3270
9°	.1564	.9877	.1584	54°	.8090	.5878	1.3764
10°	.1736	.9848	.1763	55°	.8192	.5736	1.4281
11°	.1908	.9816	.1944	56°	.8290	.5592	1.4826
12°	.2079	.9781	.2126	57°	.8387	.5446	1.5399
13°	.2250	.9744	.2309	58°	.8480	.5299	1.6003
14°	.2419	.9703	.2493	59°	.8572	.5150	1.6643
15°	.2588	.9659	.2679	60°	.8660	.5000	1.7321
16°	.2756	.9613	.2867	61°	.8746	.4848	1.8040
17°	.2924	.9563	.3057	62°	.8829	.4695	1.8807
18°	.3090	.9511	.3249	63°	.8910	.4540	1.9626
19°	.3256	.9455	.3443	64°	.8988	.4384	2.0503
20°	.3420	.9397	.3640	65°	.9063	.4226	2.1445
21°	.3584	.9336	.3839	66°	.9135	.4067	2.2460
22°	.3746	.9272	.4040	67°	.9205	.3907	2.3559
23°	.3907	.9205	.4245	68°	.9272	.3746	2.4751
24°	.4067	.9135	.4452	69°	.9336	.3584	2.6051
25°	.4226	.9063	.4663	70°	.9397	.3420	2.7475
26°	.4384	.8988	.4877	71°	.9455	.3256	2.9042
27°	.4540	.8910	.5095	72°	.9511	.3090	3.0777
28°	.4695	.8829	.5317	73°	.9563	.2924	3.2709
29°	.4848	.8746	.5543	74°	.9613	.2756	3.4874
30°	.5000	.8660	.5774	75°	.9659	.2588	3.7321
31°	.5150	.8572	.6009	76°	.9703	.2419	4.0108
32°	.5299	.8480	.6249	77°	.9744	.2250	4.3315
33°	.5446	.8387	.6494	78°	.9781	.2079	4.7046
34°	.5592	.8290	.6745	79°	.9816	.1908	5.1446
35°	.5736	.8192	.7002	80°	.9848	.1736	5.6713
36°	.5878	.8090	.7265	81°	.9877	.1564	6.3138
37°	.6018	.7986	.7536	82°	.9903	.1392	7.1154
38°	.6157	.7880	.7813	83°	.9925	.1219	8.1443
39°	.6293	.7771	.8098	84°	.9945	.1045	9.5144
40°	.6428	.7660	.8391	85°	.9962	.0872	11.4301
41°	.6561	.7547	.8693	86°	.9976	.0698	14.3007
42°	.6691	.7431	.9004	87°	.9986	.0523	19.0811
43°	.6820	.7314	.9325	88°	.9994	.0349	28.6363
44°	.6947	.7193	.9657	89°	.9998	.0175	57.2900
45°	.7071	.7071	1.0000	90°	1.0000	.0000	∞

USING LOGARITHMS
(for finding powers and roots)

The need for logarithms in arithmetic has largely disappeared with the advent of the electronic calculator. However one of the major remaining areas of usefulness is finding large or fractional powers and roots of numbers.

A theoretical discussion of logarithms is beyond the scope of this book. This practical description is offered. It explains how to deal with the logarithms of numbers greater than 1.

Each number has its corresponding logarithm, for instance:

$$\log 23.5 = 1.3711$$
$$\log 235 = 2.3711$$
$$\log 23{,}500 = 4.3711$$

A logarithm has two parts. The whole number part (which could be a 0) is called the *characteristic*. The decimal part is called the *mantissa*.

The characteristic is found by counting the whole-number digits in the number, and subtracting 1. In the examples above, 23.5 (which has 2 whole-number digits) has a characteristic of 1. The number 23,500 (which has 5 digits) has a characteristic of 4. Asking the user to determine the characteristic allows the table of logarithms to be brief and compact, yet usable for numbers of any size.

The mantissa is found by ignoring the decimal point and looking up the first three digits of the number in the table of mantissas. In the example above, 23.5, 235, and 23,500 all have the same mantissa (.3711). It was found by looking down the left-hand column for "23," then moving over to the column under "5."

The advantage of logarithms is that a number may be raised to any power by merely multiplying its logarithm by the exponent. Any root of a number may be found by dividing its logarithm by the index. For example:

$$135^{17} = (\log 135) \times 17$$
$$1.15^{120} = (\log 1.15) \times 120$$
$$9^{3.8} = (\log 9) \times 3.8$$
$$\sqrt[11]{8.6} = (\log 8.6) \div 11$$
$$\sqrt[1.5]{17} = (\log 17) \div 1.5$$

Sample Problem: Find the value of $386^{1.75}$
1. The 386 has 3 whole-number digits; therefore its characteristic is $(3 - 1)$, or 2.
2. In the table of mantissas, find "38" in the left-hand column, then move over to the column under "6," and find the mantissa of .5866.
3. We now know that log 386 = 2.5866.
4. To raise 386 to the 1.75 power, we multiply log 386 by 1.75.

$$\text{Log } 386 = 2.5866$$
$$2.5866 \times 1.75 = 4.52655$$

therefore:

(log 386) × 1.75 = 4.5266 (rounded to four places)

5. We must now find the number for which .5266 is the mantissa. We could search through the body of the table of mantissas, but the table of antilogarithms contains the same information "inside out." The mantissas are listed along the edge, and the numbers in the body of the table. Go down the left edge and find ".52." Go across to the column headed "6" and find the number 3357. But this is the number for which .5260 is the mantissa, and we want the number for .5266. Glance across on the same line, and under "6" in the Proportional Parts column, find "5." Add this to number found: 3357 + 5 = 3362.

6. Thus, 3362 is our final answer, except we do not know where the decimal point belongs. Our logarithm was 4.5266. The characteristic "4" means that there are five places before the decimal point, so our final answer is 33,620. (In finding the logarithm of a number, the characteristic was one *less* than the number of digits. In converting a logarithm back to a number, the number must have one *more* decimal place than the value of the characteristic.

This answer is correct to four significant places.

The number with which we began had only three digits, but if it had had more, it should have been rounded to four significant places. In looking up its logarithm, it would have been necessary to use the proportional parts table in precisely the same way we just did in finding the antilogarithm.

Here are five practice problems with answers correct to four significant places:

$$77^{1.25} = 228.1$$
$$1.015^{80} = 3.251$$
$$11^{3.5} = 4414$$
$$\sqrt[8]{71} = 1.704$$
$$\sqrt[1.33]{116} = 35.67$$

COMMON LOGARITHMS OF NUMBERS

N	0	1	2	3	4	5	6	7	8	9	1	2	3	4	5
											Proportional parts				
10	.0000	.0043	.0086	.0128	.0170	.0212	.0253	.0294	.0334	.0374	4	8	12	17	21
11	.0414	.0453	.0492	.0531	.0569	.0607	.0645	.0682	.0719	.0755	4	8	11	15	19
12	.0792	.0828	.0864	.0899	.0934	.0969	.1004	.1038	.1072	.1106	3	7	10	14	17
13	.1139	.1173	.1206	.1239	.1271	.1303	.1335	.1367	.1399	.1430	3	6	10	13	16
14	.1461	.1492	.1523	.1553	.1584	.1614	.1644	.1673	.1703	.1732	3	6	9	12	15
15	.1761	.1790	.1818	.1847	.1875	.1903	.1931	.1959	.1987	.2014	3	6	8	11	14
16	.2041	.2068	.2095	.2122	.2148	.2175	.2201	.2227	.2253	.2279	3	5	8	11	13
17	.2304	.2330	.2355	.2380	.2405	.2430	.2455	.2480	.2504	.2529	2	5	7	10	12
18	.2553	.2577	.2601	.2625	.2648	.2672	.2695	.2718	.2742	.2765	2	5	7	9	12
19	.2788	.2810	.2833	.2856	.2878	.2900	.2923	.2945	.2967	.2989	2	4	7	9	11
20	.3010	.3032	.3054	.3075	.3096	.3118	.3139	.3160	.3181	.3201	2	4	6	8	11
21	.3222	.3243	.3263	.3284	.3304	.3324	.3345	.3365	.3385	.3404	2	4	6	8	10
22	.3424	.3444	.3464	.3483	.3502	.3522	.3541	.3560	.3579	.3598	2	4	6	8	10
23	.3617	.3636	.3655	.3674	.3692	.3711	.3729	.3747	.3766	.3784	2	4	6	7	9
24	.3802	.3820	.3838	.3856	.3874	.3892	.3909	.3927	.3945	.3962	2	4	5	7	9
25	.3979	.3997	.4014	.4031	.4048	.4065	.4082	.4099	.4116	.4133	2	4	5	7	9
26	.4150	.4166	.4183	.4200	.4216	.4232	.4249	.4265	.4281	.4298	2	3	5	7	8
27	.4314	.4330	.4346	.4362	.4378	.4393	.4409	.4425	.4440	.4456	2	3	5	6	8
28	.4472	.4487	.4502	.4518	.4533	.4548	.4564	.4579	.4594	.4609	2	3	5	6	8
29	.4624	.4639	.4654	.4669	.4683	.4698	.4713	.4728	.4742	.4757	1	3	4	6	7
30	.4771	.4786	.4800	.4814	.4829	.4843	.4857	.4871	.4886	.4900	1	3	4	6	7
31	.4914	.4928	.4942	.4955	.4969	.4983	.4997	.5011	.5024	.5038	1	3	4	5	7
32	.5051	.5065	.5079	.5092	.5105	.5119	.5132	.5145	.5159	.5172	1	3	4	5	7
33	.5185	.5198	.5211	.5224	.5237	.5250	.5263	.5276	.5289	.5302	1	3	4	5	7
34	.5315	.5328	.5340	.5353	.5366	.5378	.5391	.5403	.5416	.5428	1	2	4	5	6
35	.5441	.5453	.5465	.5478	.5490	.5502	.5514	.5527	.5539	.5551	1	2	4	5	6
36	.5563	.5575	.5587	.5599	.5611	.5623	.5635	.5647	.5658	.5670	1	2	4	5	6
37	.5682	.5694	.5705	.5717	.5729	.5740	.5752	.5763	.5775	.5786	1	2	4	5	6
38	.5798	.5809	.5821	.5832	.5843	.5855	.5866	.5877	.5888	.5899	1	2	3	5	6
39	.5911	.5922	.5933	.5944	.5955	.5966	.5977	.5988	.5999	.6010	1	2	3	4	5
40	.6021	.6031	.6042	.6053	.6064	.6075	.6085	.6096	.6107	.6117	1	2	3	4	5
41	.6128	.6138	.6149	.6160	.6170	.6180	.6191	.6201	.6212	.6222	1	2	3	4	5
42	.6232	.6243	.6253	.6263	.6274	.6284	.6294	.6304	.6314	.6325	1	2	3	4	5
43	.6335	.6345	.6355	.6365	.6375	.6385	.6395	.6405	.6415	.6425	1	2	3	4	5
44	.6435	.6444	.6454	.6464	.6474	.6484	.6493	.6503	.6513	.6522	1	2	3	4	5
45	.6532	.6542	.6551	.6561	.6571	.6580	.6590	.6599	.6609	.6618	1	2	3	4	5
46	.6628	.6637	.6646	.6656	.6665	.6675	.6684	.6693	.6702	.6712	1	2	3	4	5
47	.6721	.6730	.6739	.6749	.6758	.6767	.6776	.6785	.6794	.6803	1	2	3	4	5
48	.6812	.6821	.6830	.6839	.6848	.6857	.6866	.6875	.6884	.6893	1	2	3	4	5
49	.6902	.6911	.6920	.6928	.6937	.6946	.6955	.6964	.6972	.6981	1	2	3	4	4
50	.6990	.6998	.7007	.7016	.7024	.7033	.7042	.7050	.7059	.7067	1	2	3	3	4
51	.7076	.7084	.7093	.7101	.7110	.7118	.7126	.7135	.7143	.7152	1	2	3	3	4
52	.7160	.7168	.7177	.7185	.7193	.7202	.7210	.7218	.7226	.7235	1	2	3	3	4
53	.7243	.7251	.7259	.7267	.7275	.7284	.7292	.7300	.7308	.7316	1	2	2	3	4
54	.7324	.7332	.7340	.7348	.7356	.7364	.7372	.7380	.7388	.7396	1	2	2	3	4
N	0	1	2	3	4	5	6	7	8	9	1	2	3	4	5

COMMON LOGARITHMS OF NUMBERS (Continued)

N	0	1	2	3	4	5	6	7	8	9	1	2	3	4	5
											Proportional parts				

Proportional parts header spans columns 1–5.

N	0	1	2	3	4	5	6	7	8	9	1	2	3	4	5
55	.7404	.7412	.7419	.7427	.7435	.7443	.7451	.7459	.7466	.7474	1	2	2	3	4
56	.7482	.7490	.7497	.7505	.7513	.7520	.7528	.7536	.7543	.7551	1	2	2	3	4
57	.7559	.7566	.7574	.7582	.7589	.7597	.7604	.7612	.7619	.7627	1	1	2	3	4
58	.7634	.7642	.7649	.7657	.7664	.7672	.7679	.7686	.7694	.7701	1	1	2	3	4
59	.7709	.7716	.7723	.7731	.7738	.7745	.7752	.7760	.7767	.7774	1	1	2	3	4
60	.7782	.7789	.7796	.7803	.7810	.7818	.7825	.7832	.7839	.7846	1	1	2	3	4
61	.7853	.7860	.7868	.7875	.7882	.7889	.7896	.7903	.7910	.7917	1	1	2	3	3
62	.7924	.7931	.7938	.7945	.7952	.7959	.7966	.7973	.7980	.7987	1	1	2	3	3
63	.7993	.8000	.8007	.8014	.8021	.8028	.8035	.8041	.8048	.8055	1	1	2	3	3
64	.8062	.8069	.8075	.8082	.8089	.8096	.8102	.8109	.8116	.8122	1	1	2	3	3
65	.8129	.8136	.8142	.8149	.8156	.8162	.8169	.8176	.8182	.8189	1	1	2	3	3
66	.8195	.8202	.8209	.8215	.8222	.8228	.8235	.8241	.8248	.8254	1	1	2	3	3
67	.8261	.8267	.8274	.8280	.8287	.8293	.8299	.8306	.8312	.8319	1	1	2	3	3
68	.8325	.8331	.8338	.8344	.8351	.8357	.8363	.8370	.8376	.8382	1	1	2	3	3
69	.8388	.8395	.8401	.8407	.8414	.8420	.8426	.8432	.8439	.8445	1	1	2	3	3
70	.8451	.8457	.8463	.8470	.8476	.8482	.8488	.8494	.8500	.8506	1	1	2	3	3
71	.8513	.8519	.8525	.8531	.8537	.8543	.8549	.8555	.8561	.8567	1	1	2	3	3
72	.8573	.8579	.8585	.8591	.8597	.8603	.8609	.8615	.8621	.8627	1	1	2	3	3
73	.8633	.8639	.8645	.8651	.8657	.8663	.8669	.8675	.8681	.8686	1	1	2	2	3
74	.8692	.8698	.8704	.8710	.8716	.8722	.8727	.8733	.8739	.8745	1	1	2	2	3
75	.8751	.8756	.8762	.8768	.8774	.8779	.8785	.8791	.8797	.8802	1	1	2	2	3
76	.8808	.8814	.8820	.8825	.8831	.8837	.8842	.8848	.8854	.8859	1	1	2	2	3
77	.8865	.8871	.8876	.8882	.8887	.8893	.8899	.8904	.8910	.8915	1	1	2	2	3
78	.8921	.8927	.8932	.8938	.8943	.8949	.8954	.8960	.8965	.8971	1	1	2	2	3
79	.8976	.8982	.8987	.8993	.8998	.9004	.9009	.9015	.9020	.9025	1	1	2	2	3
80	.9031	.9036	.9042	.9047	.9053	.9058	.9063	.9069	.9074	.9079	1	1	2	2	3
81	.9085	.9090	.9096	.9101	.9106	.9112	.9117	.9122	.9128	.9133	1	1	2	2	3
82	.9138	.9143	.9149	.9154	.9159	.9165	.9170	.9175	.9180	.9186	1	1	2	2	3
83	.9191	.9196	.9201	.9206	.9212	.9217	.9222	.9227	.9232	.9238	1	1	2	2	3
84	.9243	.9248	.9253	.9258	.9263	.9269	.9274	.9279	.9284	.9289	1	1	2	2	3
85	.9294	.9299	.9304	.9309	.9315	.9320	.9325	.9330	.9335	.9340	1	1	2	2	3
86	.9345	.9350	.9355	.9360	.9365	.9370	.9375	.9380	.9385	.9390	1	1	2	2	3
87	.9395	.9400	.9405	.9410	.9415	.9420	.9425	.9430	.9435	.9440	1	1	2	2	3
88	.9445	.9450	.9455	.9460	.9465	.9469	.9474	.9479	.9484	.9489	0	1	1	2	2
89	.9494	.9499	.9504	.9509	.9513	.9518	.9523	.9528	.9533	.9538	0	1	1	2	2
90	.9542	.9547	.9552	.9557	.9562	.9566	.9571	.9576	.9581	.9586	0	1	1	2	2
91	.9590	.9595	.9600	.9605	.9609	.9614	.9619	.9624	.9628	.9633	0	1	1	2	2
92	.9638	.9643	.9647	.9652	.9657	.9661	.9666	.9671	.9675	.9680	0	1	1	2	2
93	.9685	.9689	.9694	.9699	.9703	.9708	.9713	.9717	.9722	.9727	0	1	1	2	2
94	.9731	.9736	.9741	.9745	.9750	.9754	.9759	.9763	.9768	.9773	0	1	1	2	2
95	.9777	.9782	.9786	.9791	.9795	.9800	.9805	.9809	.9814	.9818	0	1	1	2	2
96	.9823	.9827	.9832	.9836	.9841	.9845	.9850	.9854	.9859	.9863	0	1	1	2	2
97	.9868	.9872	.9877	.9881	.9886	.9890	.9894	.9899	.9903	.9908	0	1	1	2	2
98	.9912	.9917	.9921	.9926	.9930	.9934	.9939	.9943	.9948	.9952	0	1	1	2	2
99	.9956	.9961	.9965	.9969	.9974	.9978	.9983	.9987	.9991	.9996	0	1	1	2	2
N	0	1	2	3	4	5	6	7	8	9	1	2	3	4	5

COMMON ANTILOGARITHMS

L	0	1	2	3	4	5	6	7	8	9	Proportional parts				
											1	2	3	4	5
.00	1000	1002	1005	1007	1009	1012	1014	1016	1019	1021	0	0	1	1	1
.01	1023	1026	1028	1030	1033	1035	1038	1040	1042	1045	0	0	1	1	1
.02	1047	0150	1052	1054	1057	1059	1062	1064	1067	1069	0	0	1	1	1
.03	1072	1074	1076	1079	1081	1084	1086	1089	1091	1094	0	0	1	1	1
.04	1096	1099	1102	1104	1107	1109	1112	1114	1117	1119	0	1	1	1	1
.05	1122	1125	1127	1130	1132	1135	1138	1140	1143	1146	0	1	1	1	1
.06	1148	1151	1153	1156	1159	1161	1164	1167	1169	1172	0	1	1	1	1
.07	1175	1178	1180	1183	1186	1189	1191	1194	1197	1199	0	1	1	1	1
.08	1202	1205	1208	1211	1213	1216	1219	1222	1225	1227	0	1	1	1	1
.09	1230	1233	1236	1239	1242	1245	1247	1250	1253	1256	0	1	1	1	1
.10	1259	1262	1265	1268	1271	1274	1276	1279	1282	1285	0	1	1	1	1
.11	1288	1291	1294	1297	1300	1303	1306	1309	1312	1315	0	1	1	1	2
.12	1318	1321	1324	1327	1330	1334	1337	1340	1343	1346	0	1	1	1	2
.13	1349	1352	1355	1358	1361	1365	1368	1371	1374	1377	0	1	1	1	2
.14	1380	1384	1387	1390	1393	1396	1400	1403	1406	1409	0	1	1	1	2
.15	1413	1416	1419	1422	1426	1429	1432	1435	1439	1442	0	1	1	1	2
.16	1445	1449	1452	1455	1459	1462	1466	1469	1472	1476	0	1	1	1	2
.17	1479	1483	1486	1489	1493	1496	1500	1503	1507	1510	0	1	1	1	2
.18	1514	1517	1521	1524	1528	1531	1535	1538	1542	1545	0	1	1	1	2
.19	1549	1552	1556	1560	1563	1567	1570	1574	1578	1581	0	1	1	1	2
.20	1585	1589	1592	1596	1600	1603	1607	1611	1614	1618	0	1	1	1	2
.21	1622	1626	1629	1633	1637	1641	1644	1648	1652	1656	0	1	1	2	2
.22	1660	1663	1667	1671	1675	1679	1683	1687	1690	1694	0	1	1	2	2
.23	1698	1702	1706	1710	1714	1718	1722	1726	1730	1734	0	1	1	2	2
.24	1738	1742	1746	1750	1754	1758	1762	1766	1770	1774	0	1	1	2	2
.25	1778	1782	1786	1791	1795	1799	1803	1807	1811	1816	0	1	1	2	2
.26	1820	1824	1828	1832	1837	1841	1845	1849	1854	1858	0	1	1	2	2
.27	1862	1866	1871	1875	1879	1884	1888	1892	1897	1901	0	1	1	2	2
.28	1905	1910	1914	1919	1923	1928	1932	1936	1941	1945	0	1	1	2	2
.29	1950	1954	1959	1963	1968	1972	1977	1982	1986	1991	0	1	1	2	2
.30	1995	2000	2004	2009	2014	2018	2023	2028	2032	2037	0	1	1	2	2
.31	2042	2046	2051	2056	2061	2065	2070	2075	2080	2084	0	1	1	2	2
32	2089	2094	2099	2104	2109	2113	2118	2123	2128	2133	0	1	1	2	2
.33	2138	2143	2148	2153	2158	2163	2168	2173	2178	2183	0	1	1	2	2
.34	2188	2193	2198	2203	2208	2213	2218	2223	2228	2234	1	1	2	2	3
.35	2239	2244	2249	2254	2259	2265	2270	2275	2280	2286	1	1	2	2	3
.36	2291	2296	2301	2307	2312	2317	2323	2328	2333	2339	1	1	2	2	3
.37	2344	2350	2355	2360	2366	2371	2377	2382	2388	2393	1	1	2	2	3
.38	2399	2404	2410	2415	2421	2427	2432	2438	2443	2449	1	1	2	2	3
.39	2455	2460	2466	2472	2477	2483	2489	2495	2500	2506	1	1	2	2	3
.40	2512	2518	2523	2529	2535	2541	2547	2553	2559	2564	1	1	2	2	3
.41	2570	2576	2582	2588	2594	2600	2606	2612	2618	2624	1	1	2	2	3
.42	2630	2636	2642	2649	2655	2661	2667	2673	2679	2685	1	1	2	2	3
.43	2692	2698	2704	2710	2716	2723	2729	2735	2742	2748	1	1	2	2	3
.44	2754	2761	2767	2773	2780	2786	2793	2799	2805	2812	1	1	2	3	3
.45	2818	2825	2831	2838	2844	2851	2858	2864	2871	2877	1	1	2	3	3
.46	2884	2891	2897	2904	2911	2917	2924	2931	2938	2944	1	1	2	3	3
.47	2951	2958	2965	2972	2979	2985	2992	2999	3006	3013	1	1	2	3	3
.48	3020	3027	3034	3041	3048	3055	3062	3069	3076	3083	1	1	2	3	3
.49	3090	3097	3105	3112	3119	3126	3133	3141	3148	3155	1	1	2	3	4
L	0	1	2	3	4	5	6	7	8	9	1	2	3	4	5

COMMON ANTILOGARITHMS (continued)

L	0	1	2	3	4	5	6	7	8	9	Proportional parts 1 2 3 4 5
.50	3162	3170	3177	3184	3192	3199	3206	3214	3221	3228	1 1 2 3 4
.51	3236	3243	3251	3258	3266	3273	3281	3289	3296	3304	1 1 2 3 4
.52	3311	3319	3327	3334	3342	3350	3357	3365	3373	3381	1 1 2 3 4
.53	3388	3396	3404	3412	3420	3428	3436	3443	3451	3459	1 2 2 3 4
.54	3467	3475	3483	3491	3499	3508	3516	3524	3532	3540	1 2 2 3 4
.55	3548	3556	3565	3573	3581	3589	3597	3606	3614	3622	1 2 2 3 4
.56	3631	3639	3648	3656	3664	3673	3681	3690	3698	3707	1 2 2 3 4
.57	3715	3724	3733	3741	3750	3758	3767	3776	3784	3793	1 2 3 3 4
.58	3802	3811	3819	3828	3837	3846	3855	3864	3873	3882	1 2 3 3 4
.59	3890	3899	3908	3917	3926	3936	3945	3954	3963	3972	1 2 3 4 5
.60	3981	3990	3999	4009	4018	4027	4036	4046	4055	4064	1 2 3 4 5
.61	4074	4083	4093	4102	4111	4121	4130	4140	4150	4159	1 2 3 4 5
.62	4169	4178	4188	4198	4207	4217	4227	4236	4246	4256	1 2 3 4 5
.63	4266	4276	4285	4295	4305	4315	4325	4335	4345	4355	1 2 3 4 5
.64	4365	4375	4385	4395	4406	4416	4426	4436	4446	4457	1 2 3 4 5
.65	4467	4477	4487	4498	4508	4519	4529	4539	4550	4560	1 2 3 4 5
.66	4571	4581	4592	4603	4613	4624	4634	4645	4656	4667	1 2 3 4 5
.67	4677	4688	4699	4710	4721	4732	4742	4753	4764	4775	1 2 3 4 5
.68	4786	4797	4808	4819	4831	4842	4853	4864	4875	4887	1 2 3 5 6
.69	4898	4909	4920	4932	4943	4955	4966	4977	4989	5000	1 2 3 5 6
.70	5012	5023	5035	5047	5058	5070	5082	5093	5105	5117	1 2 3 5 6
.71	5129	5140	5152	5164	5176	5188	5200	5212	5224	5236	1 2 4 5 6
.72	5248	5260	5272	5284	5297	5309	5321	5333	5346	5358	1 2 4 5 6
.73	5370	5383	5395	5408	5420	5433	5445	5458	5470	5483	1 3 4 5 6
.74	5495	5508	5521	5534	5546	5559	5572	5585	5598	5610	1 3 4 5 6
.75	5623	5636	5649	5662	5675	5689	5702	5715	5728	5741	1 3 4 5 7
.76	5754	5768	5781	5794	5808	5821	5834	5848	5861	5875	1 3 4 5 7
.77	5888	5902	5916	5929	5943	5957	5970	5984	5998	6012	1 3 4 5 7
.78	6026	6039	6053	6067	6081	6095	6109	6124	6138	6152	1 3 4 6 7
.79	6166	6180	6194	6209	6223	6237	6252	6266	6281	6295	1 3 4 6 7
.80	6310	6324	6339	6353	6368	6383	6397	6412	6427	6442	1 3 4 6 7
.81	6457	6471	6486	6501	6516	6531	6546	6561	6577	6592	2 3 5 6 8
.82	6607	6622	6637	6653	6668	6683	6699	6714	6730	6745	2 3 5 6 8
.83	6761	6776	6792	6808	6823	6839	6855	6871	6887	6902	2 3 5 6 8
.84	6918	6934	6950	6966	6982	6998	7015	7031	7047	7063	2 3 5 7 8
.85	7079	7096	7112	7129	7145	7161	7178	7194	7211	7228	2 3 5 7 8
.86	7244	7261	7278	7295	7311	7328	7345	7362	7379	7396	2 3 5 7 8
.87	7413	7430	7447	7464	7482	7499	7516	7534	7551	7568	2 4 5 7 9
.88	7586	7603	7621	7638	7656	7674	7691	7709	7727	7745	2 4 5 7 9
.89	7762	7780	7798	7816	7834	7852	7870	7889	7907	7925	2 4 6 7 9
.90	7943	7962	7980	7998	8017	8035	8054	8072	8091	8110	2 4 6 7 9
.91	8128	8147	8166	8185	8204	8222	8241	8260	8279	8299	2 4 6 8 9
.92	8318	8337	8356	8375	8395	8414	8433	8453	8472	8492	2 4 6 8 10
.93	8511	8531	8551	8570	8590	8610	8630	8650	8670	8690	2 4 6 8 10
.94	8710	8730	8750	8770	8790	8810	8831	8851	8872	8892	2 4 6 8 10
.95	8913	8933	8954	8974	8995	9016	9036	9057	9078	9099	2 4 6 8 10
.96	9120	9141	9162	9183	9204	9226	9247	9268	9290	9311	2 4 6 9 11
.97	9333	9354	9376	9397	9419	9441	9462	9484	9506	9528	2 4 6 9 11
.98	9550	9572	9594	9616	9638	9661	9683	9705	9727	9750	2 4 7 9 11
.99	9772	9795	9817	9840	9863	9886	9908	9931	9954	9977	2 5 7 9 11
L	0	1	2	3	4	5	6	7	8	9	1 2 3 4 5

THREE HUNDRED YEAR PERPETUAL CALENDAR

To find the day of the week for any date in the 19th, 20th, or 21st century:

0. Set calculator on Chain.
1. MULTIPLY year by 1.25:   **YEAR** $\boxed{\times}$ **1.25**
2. ADD correction for month:

January	6	June	3	
*leap year	5	July	5	
February	2	August	1	
*leap year	1	September	4	$\boxed{+}$ $\boxed{}$
March	2	October	6	
April	5	November	2	
May	0	December	4	

3. ADD day of the month: $\boxed{+}$ $\boxed{}$
3a. (1800s only — add 1)   (+1)
4. DIVIDE by 7: $\boxed{\div}$ $\boxed{7}$
5. Press $\boxed{=}$ key: $\boxed{=}$ XXX.xxxxx
6. SUBTRACT *whole number portion*
    only of preceding result: $\boxed{-}$ $\boxed{\text{XXX}}$
7. MULTIPLY by 7.1: $\boxed{\times}$ $\boxed{7.1}$
8. Press $\boxed{=}$ key: $\boxed{=}$ X.xxxxxxx

Whole number is the day of the week

1	Sunday	5	Thursday
2	Monday	6	Friday
3	Tuesday	0	Saturday
4	Wednesday		

*To test for leap year, divide year by 4. If *no* decimal remainder, year is leap year. Exceptions: Years 1800 and 1900 were not leap years; however, 2000 is a leap year.

CALCULATOR PROCEDURES FOR
BUSINESS PERCENTAGE PROBLEMS

Percentage problems involving buying price, selling price, profit, and markup are based on these three statements:

1) Buying Price + Profit (or Markup) = Selling Price

2) Percent Markup = $\dfrac{\text{Profit}}{\text{Buying Price}} \times 100$

3) Percent Profit = $\dfrac{\text{Profit}}{\text{Selling Price}} \times 100$

If any two of these five terms are known, the other three may be quickly found using the calculator procedures given here. The twenty possible combinations are given in convenient form so that it is only necessary to substitute the proper amounts for the words in the formula.

Other percentage problems can be thought of in these same "wholesale-retail" terms. For instance, when a government imposes an import duty, it "buys" the item, marks it up, and "sells" it again. So the problem: "If an imported item sells for $13 after the imposition of a 15% import duty, what would its price be if it were duty-free?" is the same as, "If an item sells for $13 after a 15% markup, what was its buying price?"

To quickly locate the desired procedure, find the two known terms along the top and side of the following chart. Where the row and column intersect, find the desired term. The number in parentheses tells which procedure is to be used.

Terms have been abbreviated as follows:

Buying Price, or Cost	**Cost**
Selling Price	**Sell Price**
Amount of Profit or Markup	**$ Profit**
Percent Profit	**% Profit**
Percent Markup	**% Markup**

Known → Terms ↓	Cost	Sell Price	$ Profit
% Markup	**Sell Price** (12) **$ Profit** (14)	**Cost** (11) **$ Profit** (16)	**Cost** (13) **Sell Price** (17)
% Profit	**Sell Price** (5) **$ Profit** (9)	**Cost** (6) **$ Profit** (2)	**Sell Price** (3) **Cost** (8)
$ Profit	**% Profit** (7) **% Markup** (15)	**% Profit** (1) **% Markup** (18)	
Sell Price	**% Profit** (4) **% Markup** (10)		
% Profit to **% Markup** (20)		**% Markup** to **% Profit** (19)	

These calculator procedures have been corrected for proper decimal point placement. The 25% should be entered as 25, not as .25 and 40% will appear in the display as 40.

1. **\$ Profit** $\div$ **Sell Price** $\times$ 100 $=$ % Profit
2. **Sell Price** $\times$ **% Profit** $\div$ 100 $=$ \$ Profit
3. **\$ Profit** $\div$ **% Profit** $\times$ 100 $=$ Sell Price
4. **Sell Price** $-$ **Cost** $\div$ **Sell Price** $\times$ 100 $=$ % Profit
5. **(CONST)** 100 $-$ **% Profit** $\div$ **Cost** $\div$ $=$ $=$ $\times$ 100 $=$ Sell Price
6. 100 $-$ **% Profit** $\times$ **Sell Price** $\div$ 100 $=$ Cost
7. **(CONST) Cost** $+$ **\$ Profit** $\div$ **\$ Profit** $\div$ $=$ $=$ $\times$ 100 $=$ % Profit
8. **\$ Profit** $\div$ **% Profit** $\times$ 100 $-$ **\$ Profit** $=$ Cost
9. **(CONST)** 100 $-$ **% Profit** $\div$ **Cost** $\div$ **% Profit** $\div$ $=$ $=$ \$ Profit
10. **Sell Price** $-$ **Cost** $\div$ **Cost** $\times$ 100 $=$ % Markup
11. **(CONST)** 100 $+$ **% Markup** $\div$ **Sell Price** $\div$ $=$ $=$ $\times$ 100 $=$ Cost
12. 100 $+$ **% Markup** $\times$ **Cost** $\div$ 100 $=$ Sell Price
13. **\$ Profit** $\div$ **% Markup** $\times$ 100 $=$ Cost
14. **Cost** $\times$ **% Markup** $\div$ 100 $=$ \$ Profit
15. **\$ Profit** $\div$ **Cost** $\times$ 100 $=$ % Markup
16. **(CONST)** 100 $+$ **% Markup** $\div$ **% Markup** $\div$ $=$ $=$ $\times$ **Sell Price** $=$ \$ Profit
17. 100 $+$ **% Markup** $\div$ **% Markup** $\times$ **\$ Profit** $=$ Sell Price
18. **(CONST) Sell Price** $-$ **\$ Profit** $\div$ **\$ Profit** $\div$ $=$ $=$ $\times$ 100 $=$ % Markup
19. **(CONST)** 100 $+$ **% Markup** $\div$ **% Markup** $\div$ $=$ $=$ $\times$ 100 $=$ % Profit
20. **(CONST)** 100 $-$ **% Profit** $\div$ **% Profit** $\div$ $=$ $=$ $\times$ 100 $=$ % Markup

Note: You should keep in mind as you read the following table that some calculators have a special % key which may make the " $\times$ 100" or " $\div$ 100," which appears as the last term, unnecessary.

METRIC EQUIVALENTS

LENGTH

U.S. Customary Unit	U.S. Equivalents	Metric Equivalents
inch	0.083 foot	2.54 centimeters
foot	1/3 yard, 12 inches	0.3048 meter
yard	3 feet, 36 inches	0.9144 meter
rod	5-1/2 yards, 16-1/2 feet	5.0292 meters
mile (statute, land)	1,760 yards, 5,280 feet	1.609 kilometers
mile (nautical, international)	1.151 statute miles	1.852 kilometers

AREA

U.S. Customary Unit	U.S. Equivalents	Metric Equivalents
square inch	0.007 square foot	6.4516 square centimeters
square foot	144 square inches	929.030 square centimeters
square yard	1,296 square inches, 9 square feet	0.836 square meter
acre	43,560 square feet, 4,840 square yards	4,047 square meters
square mile	640 acres	2.590 square kilometers

VOLUME OR CAPACITY

U.S. Customary Unit	U.S. Equivalents	Metric Equivalents
cubic inch	0.00058 cubic foot	16.387 cubic centimeters
cubic foot	1,728 cubic inches	0.028 cubic meter
cubic yard	27 cubic feet	0.765 cubic meter

U.S. Customary Liquid Measure	U.S. Equivalents	Metric Equivalents
fluid ounce	8 fluid drams, 1.804 cubic inches	29.573 milliliters
pint	16 fluid ounces, 28.875 cubic inches	0.473 liter
quart	2 pints, 57.75 cubic inches	0.946 liter
gallon	4 quarts, 231 cubic inches	3.785 liters
barrel	varies from 31 to 42 gallons, established by law or usage	

U.S. Customary Dry Measure	U.S. Equivalents	Metric Equivalents
pint	1/2 quart, 33.6 cubic inches	0.5506 liter
quart	2 pints, 67.2 cubic inches	1.1012 liters
peck	8 quarts, 537.605 cubic inches	8.810 liters
bushel	4 pecks, 2,150.42 cubic inches	35.238 liters

VOLUME OR CAPACITY (Continued)

British Imperial Liquid and Dry Measure	U.S. Customary Equivalents	Metric Equivalents
fluid ounce	0.961 U.S. fluid ounce, 1.734 cubic inches	28.413 milliliters
pint	1.032 U.S. dry pints, 1.201 U.S. liquid pints, 34.678 cubic inches	568.26 milliliters
quart	1.032 U.S. dry quarts 1.201 U.S. liquid quarts 69.355 cubic inches	1.136 liters
gallon	1.201 U.S. gallons, 277.420 cubic inches	4.546 liters
peck	554.84 cubic inches	0.009 cubic meter
bushel	1.032 U.S. bushels, 2,219.36 cubic inches	0.036 cubic meter

WEIGHT

U.S. Customary Unit (Avoirdupois)	U.S. Equivalents	Metric Equivalents
grain	0.036 dram, 0.002285 ounce	64.79891 milligrams
dram	27.344 grains, 0.0625 ounce	1.772 grams
ounce	16 drams, 437.5 grains	28.350 grams
pound	16 ounces, 7,000 grains	453.59237 grams
ton (short)	2,000 pounds	0.907 metric ton 907 kilograms
ton (long)	1.12 short tons, 2,240 pounds	1.016 metric tons

Apothecary Weight Unit (Drugs, etc.)	U.S. Customary Equivalents	Metric Equivalents
scruple	20 grains	1.296 grams
dram	60 grains	3.888 grams
ounce	480 grains, 1.097 avoirdupois ounce	31.103 grams
pound	5,760 grains, 0.823 avoirdupois pound	373.242 grams

WEIGHT (Continued)

Troy Weight Unit (Precious Metals, Jewels)	U.S. Customary Equivalents	Metric Equivalents
grain	1 grain	64.79891 milligrams
carat (metric)	3.086 grains	200 milligrams
pennyweight	24 grains, 0.055 avoirdupois ounce	1.555 grams
ounce	480 grains, 1.097 avoirdupois ounces	31.103 grams
pound	5,760 grains, 0.823 avoirdupois pound	373.24 grams

APPENDIX II

OPERATING THE CALCULATOR BY TOUCH

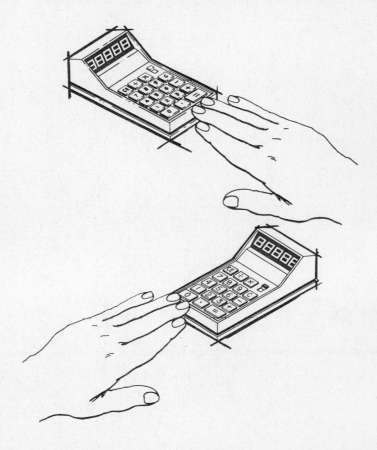

APPENDIX II
OPERATING THE CALCULATOR BY TOUCH

A typist's skills depend on finding the correct typewriter keys without looking at them. You will find your calculator more useful if you can operate it by touch. Even if you do not intend to completely master the keyboard by touch at present, you should read these instructions. Start to use the recommended finger positions so that proper habits will be established if you later decide to adopt the touch technique.

If it were possible, the ideal way to operate the calculator would be to watch three things at the same time:
1) The paper from which you are working
2) The calculator display, to verify that the correct numbers are being entered
3) The keyboard.

When the keyboard is eliminated from this list, a large improvement in speed and accuracy takes place. The eyes are then free to check the paperwork, or to check the display.

You are going to have to make a basic decision: Should you learn to operate the calculator with your right hand or your left hand? Most people are more skillful with their right hand, but if you are left-handed, the following instructions are simply reversed.

It is easy and natural to operate the calculator with the right hand, and it may never have occurred to you to use your left hand. However, if the calculator is frequently used in connection with written work that requires a pen or pencil in your right hand, much time might be saved if you could avoid putting down the pencil, moving your hand to the calculator, and possibly moving your left hand to your work to keep your place. In these circumstances, moving your idle left hand to the calculator would be very efficient.

For some of you, use of the calculator is intermittent. Many times your entries and results are handled mentally and verbally. So, if you are using the calculator in conjunction with a two-handed job that must be interrupted anyhow, then your decision should probably be to use your right hand.

If you use a telephone with buttons instead of a dial, be careful to avoid memorizing these button positions. The telephone companies have chosen to adopt a button arrange-ment inverted from the one used universally on business machines for many years. Use a different hand, or use a one-finger technique with the telephone.

Here is the way a typical calculator is arranged. We have divided it up into zones as on a typewriter. If you have a different arrangement of function keys, only slight modifica-tion of this method will give you a touch system for your calculator.

LEFT-HANDED USE   RIGHT-HANDED USE

Let's examine the construction of the calculator keyboard. The first thing to note is the small sharp point molded into the center of the 5 key. Without looking, perceive how easily you can find the 5 key just by touch. This central key is the "home" key that will establish your finger positions so you can move accurately to any desired key.

Now press one of the keys gently and observe the action of the key, and what you must do to operate it. Although the key travels a very short distance, it resists any movement until a certain amount of pressure is applied, then it collapses downward with a click that can be both heard and felt. To operate the same key a second time, you must actually relieve the pressure on it, then apply pressure again. A conscious movement of your finger is required to make the key operate, and it is most unlikely that a tremor of the hands would make a key operate in error.

Observe that you can rest your fingers freely on the keyboard and move them about. You can feel for various keys, with no chance of making an accidental entry because of the projection in the center of the 5 key. This design is the result of a great deal of study, and represents the best compromise between ease of operation and protection against erroneous entries.

Close your eyes and explore the keyboard by touch for a few minutes. Locate the keys; operate some of them.

Because the following instructions will apply equally well to either hand, we want to label the fingers in a way that will be applicable to either left-hand or right-hand operation.

The 1 finger is the finger that operates the column with the 1 in it. This is the third finger of the left hand and the first finger of the right hand. Neither little finger is used.

The 2 finger operates the column of keys with the 2 in it. It is the middle finger for both hands.

The 3 finger operates the column of keys which includes the 3 key. This is the forefinger of the left hand and the third finger of the right hand. This finger also operates the column of function keys down the right side of the keyboard.

Now we have a small project for you. We want you to
make a shield which will permit you to operate the
calculator, permit you to see the display, yet conceal the
keys from you. You learn best when you can instantly
confirm that you have done something right, therefore we
want you to be able to see each number on the display as you
enter it.

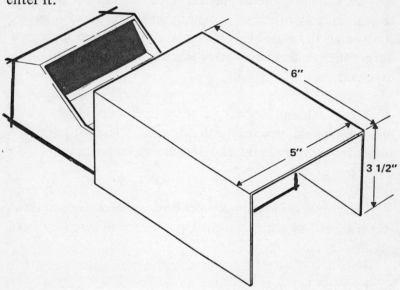

A cardboard shoebox is ideal. Cut out one end, leaving a
little piece at each corner for bracing, then cut the box right
across the middle, so it is about six inches long. If you don't
have a shoebox or a similar box, make one out of cardboard
and cellophane tape. The one important requirement is that
there be enough "headroom" so your hand can operate the
calculator without constantly bumping the top of the box.

Place the diagram of the calculator for the hand you are
going to use on the top of the box so that you can refer to it
freely. Later, when you are confident you know where the

keys are, and which fingers operate them, it can be removed, but the present goal is to avoid making mistakes if at all possible.

Switch the calculator on, sit comfortably, adjust the shield so that only the display is visible, and spend a few minutes exploring the calculator by touch, naming each key to yourself as you locate it. When you begin to feel at home, start doing the following exercises. Each exercise should be done until you feel completely familiar with it, then go on to the next one.

You should not work for more than 30 minutes at a time, but you should practice regularly. Short frequent sessions that end before your interest lags are of far more value than long boring ones.

Each time you resume practicing, go back two or three exercises and repeat them until you are again sure you have mastered them.

Exercise 1: Home Key

With your 2 finger, find the ⒌ key with the small projection on it. Enter **5 5**, checking the display. Then withdraw your hand and lift your arm from the table slightly. Return, find the ⒌ key, and enter **5 5**. When this has been repeated four times, the display will be filled with 5s. With the 3 finger, search for the ⒞ key. Clear the calculator and repeat. It is obvious that the instant and accurate locating of the ⒌ key is crucial to the entire process. This exercise should be used as a warm-up at subsequent sessions until it can be done completely automatically.

Although your thumb is not used for any of the keys, you will find it falls naturally against the corner of the calculator. It provides another guide for the position of your hand. You may find that your little finger falls similarly on the other side of the case.

Exercise 2: 8 5, 2 5

With the 2 finger, locate the $\boxed{5}$ key, then move up to the $\boxed{8}$ key. Enter **8 5 8 5 8 5 8 5** $\boxed{c}$. Use the 3 finger for the $\boxed{c}$ key. Now, in the same way, locate the $\boxed{2}$ key and enter 2 5 2 5 2 5 2 5 $\boxed{c}$. Repeat several times.

As you do these exercises, you should say the numbers to yourself, or even aloud, if you prefer. You are striving to set up an automatic association between the thought of a number and a certain movement of your fingers.

Exercise 3: 4 5, 7 5, 1 5

Enter **4 5 4 5 4 5 4 5** $\boxed{c}$ Then **7 5 7 5 7 5 7 5** $\boxed{c}$. Then 1 5 1 5 1 5 1 5 $\boxed{c}$. Repeat until confident.

The continuous operation of the calculator with your hand in one rigid position is artificial and may cause discomfort. Remove your hand from the calculator between exercises, and feel free to move the calculator and shield to vary your position.

Exercise 4: 6 5, 9 5, 3 5

Enter 6 5 6 5 6 5 6 5 [c] . Then
9 5 9 5 9 5 9 5 [c]. Then 3 5 3 5 3 5 3 5.

Be sure to check the display. The number at the extreme
right is the one just entered and should be the center of
attention. Remember to say each number at the exact
moment it is entered. Eye, finger, and mind should all work
together.

Exercise 5: 5 0

Enter 5 0 5 0 5 0 5 0 [c] . Then remove your
hand completely, return it and try to find your place
instantly. Repeat 5 0 sequence. Be conscious of your
thumb against the corner of the calculator.

Exercise 6: 1 0, 4 0, 7 0

With the 2 finger resting consciously on the [5] key,
enter 1 0 1 0 1 0 1 0 [c] . Repeat with 4 0 and
7 0.

If you have been working from the beginning of these
exercises, this might be the time to take a break. When you
resume, go back to Exercise 1 and enter only the numbers in
the title of each exercise. Repeat the entire exercise when
you make an error or feel unsure of the key location. This
should be standard procedure after a break.

Exercise 7: 5 $\boxed{\cdot}$

Enter **5** $\boxed{\cdot}$ **5** $\boxed{\cdot}$ **5** $\boxed{\cdot}$ **5** $\boxed{\cdot}$, until the display is filled, then $\boxed{c}$. The 5s will fill the display, but the decimal point will move back and forth between the first and second positions. Both of these keys are operated with the same finger.

Exercise 8: 7 9, 7 6, 7 3

Enter **7 9 7 9 7 9 7 9** $\boxed{c}$. Note that these keys are operated with the 1 and 3 fingers, with the 2 finger idle. Follow standard procedure with **7 6**, and **7 3**.

Don't fall into the trap of striving for raw speed. There should be a definite, conscious association of finger movement, eye-check of register, and verbalization of the number. Each keystroke should be deliberate and careful.

Exercise 9: 4 9, 4 6, 4 3

Enter **4 9 4 9 4 9 4 9** $\boxed{c}$. The $\boxed{c}$ key is operated with the same 3 finger that operates the $\boxed{9}$. Repeat with **4 6** and **4 3**. The 2 finger is again idle.

Exercise 10: 1 9, 1 6, 1 3

Follow the usual procedure of filling the register, then $\boxed{c}$, with these three pairs of numbers.

Exercise 11: 9 8, 6 8, 3 8

Again, the established procedure with these three pairs.

Exercise 12: 7 8, 4 8, 1 8

Let's introduce a little more variety now that you are familiar with the keys. Enter **7 8, 4 8, 1 8** [c] . Repeat until perfected. Be sure you check the display.

Now that you know the positions of all of the digits and the [c] key, try a little variation. Go into a room that is only faintly lit — too dimly lit to see the keyboard — and invent exercises of your own, watching the display. Enter **1 2 3 4 5**, then backwards. Enter **2 4 6 8, 1 3 5 7**, Social Security numbers, birthday dates. Do *not* continue if you are making errors.

Exercise 13: 9 2, 6 2, 3 2

Enter **9 2, 6 2, 3 2** [c] . Repeat until mastered.

Exercise 14: 7 2, 4 2, 1 2

Enter **7 2, 4 2, 1 2** [c] . If you become confused about the location of the [2] key, return and locate the [5] key by its point, then move to [2] .

Exercise 15: 9 0, 6 0, 3 0

Return to the old procedure of entering
9 0 9 0 9 0 9 0 [c] . This is a long stretch. Repeat
until thoroughly mastered. Then similarly with **6 0**
and **3 0**.

Exercise 16: 7 [·] **, 4** [·] **, 1** [·]

Begin this exercise with **7** [·] **7** [·] until the
display is filled, then [c] . Repeat with **4** [·] and
1 [·] . Then review with **7** [·] **, 4** [·] **, 1** [·] [c] .
Remember that the decimal key is operated with the
2 finger.

Exercise 17: 9 [·] **, 6** [·] **, 3** [·]

Follow the same procedure as in Exercise 16.

Exercise 18: 0 [·] **, 2** [·] **, 8** [·]

Follow the same procedure as in Exercise 16.

Exercise 19: 7 3, 1 9, 4 6

Enter **7 3 7 3 7 3 7 3** [c] . Then perform same
procedure with **1 9** and **4 6**. This exercise takes you
to the corners of the keyboard with the 2 finger idle.
Then review by entering **7 3, 1 9, 4 6**.

Exercise 20: 7 9, 4 6, 1 3

Follow the same procedure as in Exercise 19.

You should now have complete mastery of all the number keys and the ⌈c⌉ key. If in subsequent exercises you find you make frequent errors with one number, go back and find the exercise among the preceding ones that drills the number that troubles you.

Exercise 21: ⌈+⌉ Key and Number Review

Add the following numbers. The ⌈+⌉ key and the ⌈=⌉ key are both operated by the 3 finger. Each of these sums totals 999, so that there is a double-check of the accuracy of each entry. It is *not* necessary to operate the ⌈c⌉ key between problems.

482 ⌈+⌉ 517 ⌈=⌉   639 ⌈+⌉ 360 ⌈=⌉

851 ⌈+⌉ 148 ⌈=⌉   390 ⌈+⌉ 609 ⌈=⌉

234 ⌈+⌉ 765 ⌈=⌉   862 ⌈+⌉ 137 ⌈=⌉

789 ⌈+⌉ 210 ⌈=⌉   509 ⌈+⌉ 490 ⌈=⌉

522 ⌈+⌉ 477 ⌈=⌉   648 ⌈+⌉ 351 ⌈=⌉

Exercise 22: ⌈−⌉ Key and Number Review

Subtract the following numbers. In each answer, all three digits are the same, but the three digits are not the same in every problem.

892 ⌈−⌉ 337 ⌈=⌉   978 ⌈−⌉ 534 ⌈=⌉

704 ⌈−⌉ 260 ⌈=⌉   685 ⌈−⌉ 574 ⌈=⌉

342 ⌈−⌉ 120 ⌈=⌉   906 ⌈−⌉ 129 ⌈=⌉

689 ⌈−⌉ 356 ⌈=⌉   686 ⌈−⌉ 242 ⌈=⌉

574 ⌈−⌉ 463 ⌈=⌉   850 ⌈−⌉ 517 ⌈=⌉

Exercise 23. Mixed + and − Keys

Perform the following chain calculations. The answer to each problem is 0.

2 + 4 − 7 + 1 =   4 − 1 + 2 − 5 =
1 − 3 + 9 − 7 =   3 + 5 − 9 + 1 =
6 + 2 − 9 + 1 =   8 − 6 + 1 − 3 =
4 − 8 + 6 − 2 =   3 + 5 − 9 + 1 =
5 + 3 − 7 − 1 =   7 − 8 + 6 − 5 =

Exercise 24: · and 0

Enter each of the following numbers, check the display for correctness, and clear.

.0056	9.675
1.038	8.0004
7.0078	5.538
5.925	8.00625
.00314	7.714

Repeat as necessary until you are fully confident.

Exercise 25: × Key

The × key is operated by the 3 finger. Watch your finger placement chart carefully while you do the following multiplication problems:

3 × 8 =   9 × 4 =
6 × 2 =   3 × 7 =
9 × 5 =   6 × 1 =

Exercise 26: ÷ Key

The ÷ key is operated by the 2 finger. Perform the following division operations. For convenience in checking, all results are 2.

90 ÷ 45 =   84 ÷ 42 =
36 ÷ 18 =   12 ÷ 6 =
74 ÷ 37 =   46 ÷ 23 =
66 ÷ 33 =   58 ÷ 29 =
28 ÷ 14 =   70 ÷ 35 =

Exercise 27: × and ÷ Keys, with Decimals

This exercise resembles actual operations rather than drills. The correct result is given in each case; check your result against it carefully.

57.3 × 2.56 = 146.688
81.25 × 77.3 = 6280.625
.0625 × 16 = 1
60.84 ÷ .78 = 78
9425 ÷ .325 = 29,000
.656 ÷ .41 = 1.6
7.28 × 83 ÷ .91 = 664
.1105 ÷ 130 × 11.7648 = .01
44 × 3.38 ÷ 11.44 = 13
142.857 ÷ 3 × 7 = 333.333

With the completion of Exercise 27, you should be able to operate the calculator in complete confidence without looking at the keys. If some movements are unsure, or if you are making certain errors, find the exercise dealing with that skill and repeat it until you have mastered it.

Find practice material in your own area of interest, and invent the kind of problems you actually do on the calculator. This is far more interesting than mere drill material.

You may find that you are tempted to go back to poking at the keys with one finger. Use and practice your new skills; your calculator will shortly become as natural and automatic an extension of your thoughts as writing.

APPENDIX III

SUMMARY OF OTHER FEATURES

APPENDIX III
SUMMARY OF OTHER FEATURES

The electronic calculator opens a whole new world to its user. Our aim has been to give you in these few pages a look at this new world. We have limited the scope of our book to the four-function calculator. We have focused on using only combinations of addition, subtraction, multiplication, and division. These four functions can assist you in solving a wide variety of problems.

However, as we have shown, some calculators have the ability to do "constant" calculations. By this is meant the ability to enter a number and use it over and over again in multiplication and division without reentering it. Some of the ways to use this feature have been discussed in much detail throughout the book.

Perhaps at this point we should mention the "logic" of calculator arithmetic. This means the way instructions are given to the calculator. It also means what operations are possible. There are two standard types. One of these is called **algebraic logic**. This is the logic we have used throughout the book. Here, when a number is entered, it is assumed to be positive unless otherwise indicated. For example, in order to perform:

$$5 + 6 - 8 = 3$$

on this type of calculator, we do the following sequence:

$$5 \; \boxed{+} \; 6 \; \boxed{-} \; 8 \; \boxed{=} \; 3$$

Notice that the operations are done as one would speak or write.

The second kind of logic is called **arithmetic logic**. It is commonly found on adding machines and some business-oriented calculators. This kind of logic requires that one enter the number first. Then the sign of that number is entered. Thus, on this kind of calculator the above expression is entered in the following sequence:

$$5 \; \boxed{+} \; 6 \; \boxed{+} \; 8 \; \boxed{\equiv} \; 3$$

Briefly, let us mention other features that may be found on some calculators. We shall only sketch the meanings of these features.

First, there may be a **percent** key. Here are examples of how this key can be used.

What is 6% of 1250?

1250 $\boxed{\times}$ 6 $\boxed{\%}$ 75

Thus, we see that the decimal is automatically positioned for us.

What percent of 8 is 4? The answer is obtained as follows:

$$4 \; \boxed{\div} \; 8 \; \boxed{\%} \; 50$$

Another common feature is the choice of **full-floating** or **pre-set** decimal point. The calculator we have been discussing has a full-floating decimal point. Let us divide 2514 by 15. Using a full-floating decimal, the answer would be displayed as

167.5

On the other hand, if we pre-set the calculator to allow for four places, we get

167.5000

Notice the added zeros on the end. Conventional adding machines use a fixed decimal point, usually with two places to right of the decimal always reserved.

Some calculators are equipped with a **square root** key ($\sqrt{x}$), and a key that **squares** a number (x^2). For example, to find $\sqrt{6.25}$:

6.25 $\sqrt{x}$ 2.5

On the other hand to find 2^2:

2 x^2 4

A **reciprocal** key, $1/x$, automatically divides the number "1" by the entered number. Thus:

2 $1/x$ .5

As calculators become more sophisticated, other special keys are provided. These keys are designed to save you the trouble of looking things up in a table. For example, calculators that are designed for engineers and scientists may have keys that automatically convert degrees to radians and radians to degrees in angle measurement. Others may also have keys to find the sine, cosine, and tangent of angles. Some calculators have log and exponential tables built into them.

Special business functions are built into some calculators. These calculators can find averages, compute present values of an annuity, and compute finance charge amortization by the "rule of 78s."

In the future, we should expect many more added features to aid in our computational needs. It is clear that even small electronic calculators have already come a long way beyond mechanical calculators.